Farming with Soil Life

A Handbook for Supporting Soil Invertebrates and Soil Health on Farms

Jennifer Hopwood

Stephanie Frischie

Emily May

Eric Lee-Mäder

The Xerces Society for Invertebrate Conservation

xerces.org

Published by the Sustainable Agriculture Research and Education (SARE, sare.org) program, with funding from the National Institute of Food and Agriculture, U.S. Department of Agriculture.

The Xerces® Society for Invertebrate Conservation is a nonprofit organization that protects wildlife through the conservation of invertebrates and their habitat. Established in 1971, the Society is at the forefront of invertebrate protection, harnessing the knowledge of scientists and the enthusiasm of citizens to implement conservation programs worldwide. The Society uses advocacy, education, and applied research to promote invertebrate conservation.

The Xerces Society for Invertebrate Conservation
628 NE Broadway, Suite 200, Portland, OR 97232
Tel (855) 232-6639   Fax (503) 233-6794   xerces.org

Regional offices coast to coast.

The Xerces Society is an equal opportunity employer and provider. Xerces® is a trademark registered in the U.S. Patent and Trademark Office.

This book was written and designed by the Xerces Society, with support from Northeast Sustainable Agriculture Research and Education (SARE) grant ENE19-158, Organic Valley and Xerces Society members. It is published by the SARE program, with funding from the USDA's National Institute of Food and Agriculture (NIFA) under cooperative agreement number 2022-28640-37487.

Ordering Information

Visit www.sare.org/farming-for-soil-life or call (301) 374-9696. Discounts are available for orders in quantity.

Acknowledgments

The authors would like to thank Angela Laws (the Xerces Society) for contributing to the section on climate change and Liz Robertson (the Xerces Society) for sourcing photos. We thank the following for their careful review and input on early drafts of this publication: Rick Clark (Clark Land and Cattle); Kelly Gill (the Xerces Society); Scott Black (the Xerces Society); Mace Vaughan (the Xerces Society); Daniel Kane (Yale University); Barry Fisher (National Soil Health Division, USDA-NRCS); and James Nardi, Ph.D. (University of Illinois).

The authors are especially grateful to Jim Nardi for his generosity in granting us permission to include his illustrations from *Life in the Soil: A Guide for Naturalists and Gardeners* (2007. 293 pp. Illinois: University of Chicago Press).

Editing: Krystal Eldridge, The Xerces Society

Additional editing and layout: Sara Morris, The Xerces Society

Citation

Hopwood, J., S. Frischie, E. May, and E. Lee-Mäder. 2021. *Farming with Soil Life: A Handbook for Supporting Soil Invertebrates and Soil Health on Farms*. 128 pp. Portland, OR: The Xerces Society for Invertebrate Conservation.

Photographs and Artwork

We are grateful to the many photographers and designers for allowing us to use their wonderful photographs. The copyright for all photographs is retained by the creators. None of the photographs may be reproduced without permission from the creator. For a complete list of photographers, please see "Additional Acknowledgments" on page 125.

Disclaimer

Library of Congress Control Number: 2023902904

Farming with Soil Life: A Handbook for Supporting Soil Invertebrates and Soil Health on Farms

Contents

Our Living Soil: An Introduction

Typically, if soil gets much attention from the general public, it is simply for how well (or poorly) plants grow in it. Soil science—an incredibly rich, complex, and multifaceted academic discipline—has long recognized that Earth's soils are a dynamic interaction of physical, chemical, and biological properties. Yet most of us rarely give any thought to the fact that the ground beneath our feet is a complicated, ever-moving tangle of rocks and animals and plants and water and chemical compounds that rivals the ocean as a wild, dark, mysterious, and inscrutable realm.

When we have focused on soil, it has often been to solve practical questions that arise: How do I keep this stuff from washing away? What's the best way to till this dirt? What chemicals can I add so the tomatoes stop getting blossom-end rot?

Our understanding and thinking continues to change. Farmers, conservationists, scientists, and others fascinated by soils have started pushing us all to ask questions about what lives in the soil. For the first time, there is a nationwide conversation about the paramount importance of soil biology.

It turns out this biology question is key to many environmental and economic questions of our time. Increasingly, we understand that healthy soils are productive and resilient, ultimately sustaining abundant crops with fewer costly inputs down the road. For reasons that we are just beginning to understand, the biology of certain soils can also suppress plant diseases, much in the same way a healthy gut biome in people might help prevent human diseases. There's also mounting evidence that we can harness the incredible root systems of plants and their microbial allies to store vast quantities of atmospheric carbon dioxide in Earth's soils at rates that could help offset human-generated greenhouse gas. And, as we continue to face a striking global loss of wild plants and animals, we are becoming more aware that soil is part of the fundamental ecology of all species—it provides a living platform for tigers and crickets, bacteria and bees, oaks and wildflowers, as well as the minerals that build not only the cells of those species but also our own.

This publication is our addition to the discussion on soil biology. It is impossible to tell the story of every living species connected to the ground beneath us. With that in mind, we have focused this guide on the diverse, often overlooked, and essential living species that we know best: the major invertebrates (macrofauna and mesofauna) found in temperate agricultural soils. There is a focus on North America in the groups of organisms and the soil health practices that are covered, but many groups are present in these soil types around the world, and the same management principles apply. Larger soil animals, such as ground beetles, woodlice, and springtails, and their many companions, have received less attention than soil microbes in recent years. We hope this publication helps fill that gap.

FIGURE 1—Soil is a living environment that connects above ground with below ground, and mineral with biological.

FIGURE 2—The bare, exposed and eroding soils of the Dust Bowl during the 1930s were caused by disruption of soil through excessive and extensive tilling that removed perennial vegetation (grasslands) in the Plains, where periods of drought and high winds are typical. (Photo: Arthur Rothstein, Library of Congress.)

Finally, we acknowledge the many thoughtful soil conservation pioneers who laid the groundwork for this effort. Most notably, faced with the great Dust Bowl of the 1930s that threatened the entire economic and environmental foundation of the United States, we survived thanks to the innovative work of the U.S. Department of Agriculture (USDA) Soil Conservation Service (now the Natural Resources Conservation Service), as well as local conservation districts and individual farmers. We all owe that earlier generation of soil conservationists a debt of gratitude, just as we all owe you, the reader, our gratitude for taking up this same cause.

A Short History of Soil

Soil is being made continuously all around us through the slow decomposition and disintegration of larger mineral and carbon components. The most abundant of these objects, on a planetary scale, is the bedrock of Earth itself.

Bedrock is created across a timeframe as old as Earth's. For example, the accumulated skeletons of ancient animals may become compressed in marine sediments to create limestone. The rise and fall of seas, movement of tectonic plates, eruption of volcanoes, and other factors recycle and rearrange Earth's geology into mountain ranges or eroded canyons. Flowing, freezing, and thawing water; glacial movement; the chemistry of our atmosphere; the cycling of nutrients and energy through organisms in the soil; and other forces work to constantly disintegrate the upper layers of rock across the planet. In soil science, these forces are collectively referred to as weathering and are broadly divided into physical weathering (such as abrasion) and chemical weathering (such as oxidation). The weathered particles of all this rock (referred to as parent material) may remain as semi-stable fragments for long periods, or they may dissolve as minerals into water. Weathering creates smaller particles from the parent material. These particles are transported and deposited by gravity, water, wind, and glaciers.

Of course, soil has organic origins along with mineral sources. Once rock is weathered into smaller particles, plant roots can grow within it, and this begins the transformation of mineral pieces into soil. This mixing, ongoing disintegration, and recombination of organic and inorganic parent materials creates our soils. Most of those actions are dependent on (or at least are carried out most efficiently by) the life in our soils, especially fungi, plant roots, and—most dynamically—animals. Roots create an environment for microorganisms and mesofauna and, as organic matter builds up, for larger animals and plants. Some soil organic matter, such as peat, can be ancient, forming as dead vegetation that accumulates in wetlands, eventually filling up wetlands with thick, relatively stable organic residue that can persist for centuries. On upland locations, soil is constantly accumulating through the deposition of dead vegetation, dead animals, and dead plant roots. Soils tell the stories of a landscape's history.

The Functions of Soil

Soils provide many practical services that combine to make the world a livable place. Some of these services are so obvious that we tend to take them for granted, while others are mostly invisible and so large that they can be challenging to measure or document. These are among the most valuable things that soils provide us:

- **A medium for plant growth:** Soils not only provide a physical anchor for plant roots but also function as a sponge that absorbs water, air, and nutrients, slowly releasing those materials to sustain plant growth. Soil also protects plants from disease, pests, and stress.

- **Water-supply regulation and filtration:** The infiltration of rainwater and snowmelt into soil is made possible by pores between soil particles and by openings created by plant roots and animal tunnels. Some of this water is retained in soil pores and even pulled upward against the force of gravity through capillary action. This spongelike property of soils, known as water-holding capacity, is variable depending on the texture of soils. By holding onto water, soils slow the water's dispersal rate and reduce the potential for flooding. Soil is also the Earth's largest natural water filter; as water passes through soil into groundwater reserves, various physical, chemical, and biological processes filter contaminants - binding to, degrading, or otherwise removing contaminants from groundwater used for drinking or irrigation.

- **Recycling and storage of organic matter:** Most terrestrial plants and animals ultimately become soil when they die. Decomposition by fungi, bacteria, insects, and other soil organisms transforms once-living plants and animals into forms that can be used by other living things as energy sources for growth and maintenance. Some organic matter is also locked away into semi-stable forms of carbon that can remain in soil for centuries. This ability to sequester carbon remains one of the most attention-grabbing properties of soils and has the potential to play a major role in mitigating climate change.

- **Habitat for wildlife:** This guide is mostly about the insects and other invertebrate animals that live in soil; however, many animals—ranging from burrowing owls to tortoises to foxes—also nest, burrow, or hibernate in soil. Even some very large animals, including bears and alligators, excavate underground dens. In many cases, secondary inhabitants, including creatures such as snakes or bumble bees (which might occupy tunnel systems excavated by rodents), move into burrows created by other animals. The impact that some of these animals have on soils is not often considered, yet the churning, mixing, and rearranging of soils performed by animals can be significant. It's estimated that in some areas, ants move more than a ton of soil per acre, per year. This tunneling activity moves organic matter on the soil surface below ground and brings subsoil to the surface, creating a mixed substrate and adding macropores that allow air and water movement within soil.

- **An engineering medium:** Soil is the foundation (or construction material) for roads as well as homes, bridges, buildings, and countless other structures. Different types of soil have variable bearing strength, compressibility, seismic stability, and potential to swell or shrink. These and other engineering considerations are often influenced by fundamental soil properties such as particle size, mineral types, bulk density, and more.

FIGURE 3—Soil provides many essential functions, including (clockwise from left): a medium in which plant life can grow (cover crop workshop), water supply and filtration (seen during this infiltration demonstration), recycling and storing organic matter (here a farmer uses a soil probe to check organic matter depth), and shelter for a variety of animals (like groundhogs and bumble bee colonies).

How Soils Are Classified

Soil is the dynamic natural body of mineral and organic matter that covers terrestrial Earth. This body changes over time as climate and living organisms act upon the rocks and organic matter from which soil is created, called parental material.

Because climate and bedrock vary significantly across the globe, the resulting types of soil found on Earth also differ greatly from location to location. To help us understand and compare soil types, various systems of soil classification have been developed. These classification systems use a taxonomic hierarchy to categorize soils in specific locations, similar to the taxonomic hierarchies used to classify plants and animals.

In the case of soils, the classification hierarchy consists of distinct orders, suborders, great groups, subgroups, families, series, and phases. Soil orders are the classification level for applied use. Orders can be based on age or weathering status (inceptisol, entisol, oxisol), reflect what grew there (mollisol, spodosol), or have been shaped by hydrological influences (aridisol, histosol). Farming occurs on all soil orders, but certain orders are better for production than others. Along with this classification system, soil scientists have created specialized terminology for describing soil architecture.

Setting aside formal soil classification, at a general level—such as when comparing different types of farm soils—we typically group soils according to texture based on the relative percentage of sand, clay, and silt in any given soil sample. Each of these mineral particles is formally defined by a size range, and their specific combination in any given soil sample influences physical and chemical properties, such as bulk density, water-holding capacity, hydraulic conductivity, porosity, the exchange and absorption of ions, and more.

Along with soil texture, soil organic matter (SOM) influences soil properties and the way we categorize different soils. SOM is the fraction of the soil consisting of various plant and animal residues. There are several categories of SOM that differ in chemical composition and stage of decomposition, and the majority of SOM was originally plant residues. Some types of SOM are forms that are readily available food sources for soil microorganisms. Other types of SOM are long-lived and resistant to further breakdown. These store and release carbon over months and years. Management practices alter total organic carbon and the proportion of carbon present in each category. One aspect of farming for soil function and health is to understand how management practices affect SOM.

Finally, we often group soils by moisture categories. Very dry, well-drained soils may be described as xeric, while soils that are saturated with water for extended periods are known as hydric. Soils with a relatively even balance of moisture are called mesic and represent the primary soils used for agricultural production.

FIGURE 4—Particle size and aggregrate stability are two physical traits of soil.

Soil Properties

Soils are a fascinating mix of living and nonliving things. On some levels, they function as a superorganism—an enormous singular living thing made up of many smaller living things. In other ways, soils function as an amalgamation of rock and mineral particles. Soils are both alive and not alive at the same time. This condition provides us with an interesting mix of physical, chemical, and biological properties that can be readily observed. This section provides a basic catalog of some of the most fundamental properties in each of those categories.

Physical Properties

- **Texture:** Nonorganic soil particles are classified by size into clay (small), silt (medium), and sand (large). Of these, clay has uniquely small pores and electric charges around its particles, which retain water and bind with nutrients. The ratio of these three particles relative to each other is a basic way of defining a soil's type, such as a silt loam or a sandy loam.

- **Structure and aggregates:** Soil particles form aggregates, which are particles bound by organic or mineral compounds. Soils can be evaluated by how those aggregates hold together or resist deformation when crushed. Healthy soils have good aggregate stability—the soil resists compaction and the pore spaces that are important for root growth, animal movement, water infiltration, and gas exchange remain intact. Powdery soil or soil with large, hard clods are examples of poor soil structure.

- **Bulk density:** The weight of soil relative to its volume is an indicator of how much pore space exists between the particles. This property is commonly measured in grams per cubic centimeter, with higher numbers reflecting less pore space. Because organic matter provides an abundance of pore spaces, even the addition of a small amount of organic matter can reduce the bulk density of a soil.

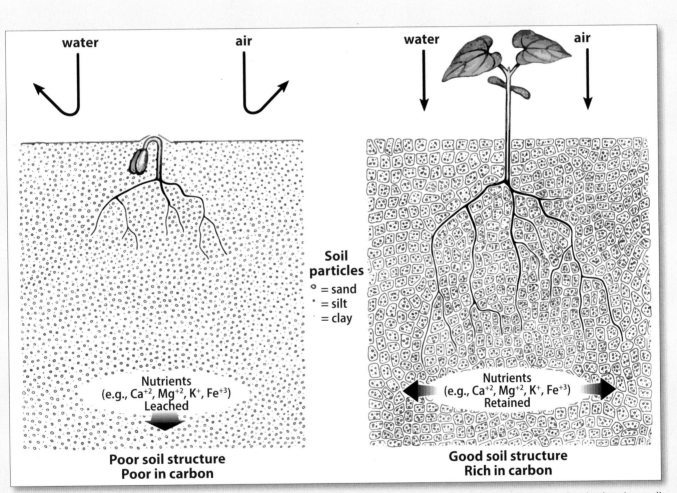

FIGURE 5—Poor soil structure (left) restricts the inflow of water and air and limits root growth. Important cations are leached and overall carbon is low. In contrast, soils with good structure (right) have more space for air, water, roots, and animals, and chemical cycles related to plant health are more likely to function well, including carbon storage and movement (Adapted from J. Nardi 2007, University of Chicago Press).

Biological Properties

- **Nutrient cycling:** One of the most important services that soil organisms perform is the decomposition of organic matter (such as dead plants and animals) into smaller pieces, which then have greater proportions of surface area. Mineralization is the further decomposition and transformation of organic matter into nutrients available for plants. This combined process, called nutrient cycling, especially the cycling of nitrogen and carbon, is a critical factor in soil fertility. Soil microbes have historically received most of the attention for nutrient cycling, yet larger organisms also play key roles. The roles of soil invertebrates can be categorized as: ecosystem engineers that create and maintain habitat; herbivores and predators that regulate the populations of other organisms; and primary decomposers that accelerate the decomposition process by breaking down plant or animal material into pieces more accessible to microorganisms.

- **Microbial diversity and abundance:** Each combination of soil characteristics, time, and conditions shape microbial communities. The composition of species that are present (diversity) and quantity of each (abundance) will drive different ecosystem services. For example, arbuscular mycorrhizae (types of fungi) and rhizobia (types of bacteria) make phosphorus and nitrogen more available to plant roots for uptake. Saprotrophic fungi cycle nutrients by breaking down leaf litter near the soil surface and mineralizing carbon.

The Nitrogen Cycle

Nitrogen is an essential chemical element for life on Earth and is present in many different compounds. The transformation and reuse of nitrogen in biological and geochemical processes is described in the nitrogen cycle.

Bacteria and other microbes are the natural key in the terrestrial nitrogen cycle. Soil is the interface where nitrogen fixation occurs and where reactive forms of nitrogen are held and taken up by plants. Nearly 70% of the atmosphere is nitrogen gas (N_2), but this form of nitrogen is nonreactive and is not biologically available to most life forms. For example, we humans take in nitrogen with each breath, but we exhale it. Our intake of usable nitrogen comes via the plant and animal ingredients in our food.

But how did it get from the atmosphere into plants and animals? We have bacteria to thank. Nitrogen-fixing bacteria grow in close symbiosis within specialized structures, called nodules, in the roots of certain plant species. The majority of plants in the bean, or legume, family (Fabaceae) share symbiotic relationships with one or more nitrogen-fixing bacteria.

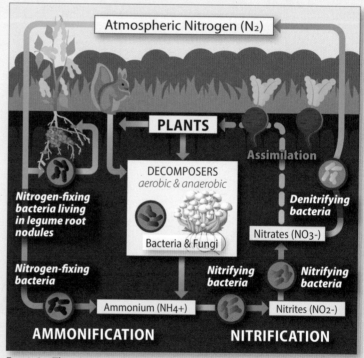

FIGURE 6—The nitrogen cycle.

Symbiotic nitrogen fixation also occurs in more than 30 non-legume plant genera. There are other groups of bacteria that live freely in the soil and also fix nitrogen. Nitrogen-fixing bacteria take in atmospheric nitrogen from soil pore spaces and convert it to organic nitrogen. Bacteria and fungi decompose dead plants or animals and also convert the nitrogen in those tissues to ammonia. Groups of nitrifying bacteria convert ammonia to ammonium, ammonium to nitrite (NO_2-) and then nitrite to nitrate (NO_3-), which is the form of nitrogen available for plants to take up. Denitrifying bacteria convert nitrate back to atmospheric nitrogen.

Apart from biological nitrogen fixation, additional energy can convert atmospheric nitrogen to biologically usable forms. High enough levels of energy to fix nitrogen occur naturally via lightning and through the manmade Haber-Bosch process, which uses high pressure, high temperatures, and natural gas.

Chemical Properties

- **Cation-exchange capacity:** Elements that occur in soil sometimes exist as positively charged ions, called cations. Aluminum, magnesium, potassium, calcium, and hydrogen are some of the common cations found in soils. In contrast, small soil particles such as clay and organic matter have negatively charged surfaces that attract these cations, slowing the rate at which they are leached out of the soil by water. Despite this, some cations are inevitably lost or taken up by plants. When this happens, those lost cations may be replaced by others in a process called cation exchange. The measure of negative charges in a unit of soil that can rapidly exchange cations is called the cation-exchange capacity. (To put it another way, it is the measure of how many cations a soil sample can hold in an exchangeable form.) Typically, the greater the proportion of clay and organic matter in a soil, the greater the cation-exchange capacity will be, and the greater the potential will be for the soil to retain most plant nutrients.
- **Soil pH:** The acidity or alkalinity of a soil is known as the soil pH. This property is influenced by the parent material (or bedrock) from which the soil is created, as well as climate, vegetation, and other factors such as fertility management and irrigation. For example, in the northeastern United States, leaching of basic cations is one of the primary causes of soil acidification. Various plant nutrients are soluble at different ranges of pH. For many agricultural plants, a slightly acidic soil in the pH range of 6.0 to 6.8 is often preferred. Inputs used to alter the pH of a soil, such as lime or sulfur, may influence the types and abundance of soil organisms.

Other Characteristics

The following characteristics are shaped by a combination of physical, chemical, biological, and temporal influences:

- **Color:** The parent material and iron, organic matter, and other soil components create distinct soil colors that vary between locations and depths. Moreover, oxidation or other reactions can cause variations in soil color. In many cases, colors can provide clues to what materials are present in a specific soil sample, as well as whether a soil is well aerated, poorly drained, or highly weathered.
- **Horizonation:** Soils form distinct layers, called horizons, that make up a deep cross section of soil, called a soil profile. Horizons usually run parallel to the ground surface. Soil horizons are often labeled with letters of the alphabet. The top horizons (O and A) consist of the organic material and small particles typically called topsoil. Deeper horizons (such as B, C, and E) are typically made of minerals with little organic matter. Each horizon will typically have a distinct color and texture that sets it apart from the other horizons around it in a profile. (The horizon labeled O is typically found in forest soils and represents organic matter, but the other letters assigned to horizons are arbitrarily alphabetical.)

FIGURE 7—A Munsell chart is used to categorize the color of a soil.

FIGURE 8—A forest soil profile with distinct horizons.

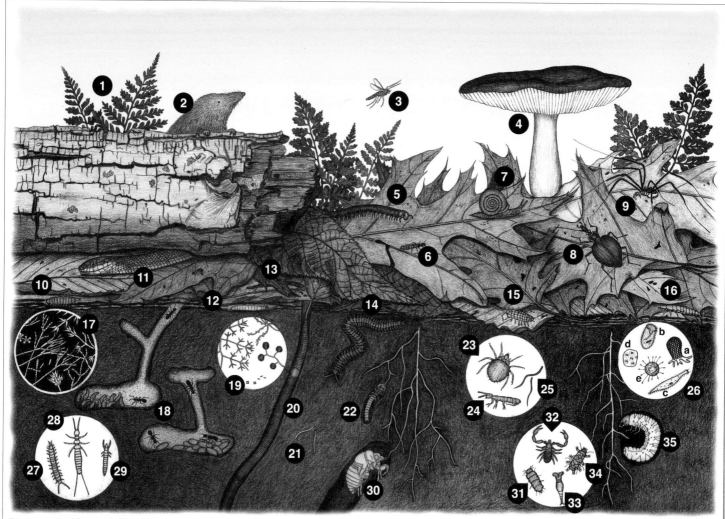

Figure 9—Healthy soil is full of life: 1—wood fern; 2—shrew; 3—March fly; 4—mycorrhizal mushroom (*Russula*); 5—millipede; 6—rove beetle; 7—snail; 8—snail-eating ground beetle; 9—daddy longlegs; 10—soldier fly larva; 11—ringneck snake; 12—crane fly larva; 13—soil flatworm; 14—soil centipede; 15—woodlouse; 16—firefly larva; 17—filaments (hyphae) of soil fungi; 18—ants with their larvae and pupae; 19—bacteria and actinomycetes; 20—earthworm; 21—potworms; 22—click beetle larva; 23—oribatid mite; 24—springtail; 25—nematodes; 26—protozoa and algae: (a) testate protozoa, (b, c) ciliated protozoa, (d) blue-green alga, (e) heliozoa; 27—symphylan; 28—dipluran; 29—proturan; 30—cicada nymph; 31—pauropod; 32—pseudoscorpion; 33—rotifer; 34—tardigrade; 35—scarab beetle larva. (Adapted from J. Nardi 2007, University of Chicago Press.)

Soil is Full of Life

Beyond the nonliving mineral components of soil and the dead organic matter, soil is also composed of diverse living organisms, both fauna (animals) and flora (plants, bacteria, archaea, and fungi). These organisms are classified in multiple ways, with the simplest classifications based upon their relative size and physiology. The profiles in **Chapter 6** include these groups of organisms, with brief coverage of flora and detailed focus on macrofauna and mesofauna:

- Microflora (bacteria and microscopic fungi and algae)
- Fungi (mushrooms and other macrofungi)
- Plants (mosses, lichens, liverworts, and vascular plants)
- Microfauna (protozoa)
- Mesofauna (nematodes, rotifers, tardigrades, potworms, and smaller arthropods such as springtails and mites)
- Macrofauna (larger arthropods like centipedes and beetles, isopods, mollusks, earthworms, and vertebrate animals)

American Burying Beetle

A number of beetles contribute significantly to the recycling of carrion, returning nutrients to the soil. Carrion is a small portion of detritus in most ecosystems but has an important role in nutrient cycling because it decomposes at a much faster rate than plant materials, which contain lignin, hemicellulose, and cellulose—all resistant to decomposition. Carrion is also much more nutrient rich than the same amount of plant matter. Decomposing carrion creates small islands of increased soil fertility that can have long-lasting ecological effects.

Of the 31 species of burying beetles in North America, the largest is the American burying beetle (*Nicrophorus americanus*). At more than 1.5 in. (3.81 cm) in length, adults have shiny black bodies with bright-orange bands on their wing covers, a patch of orange between their eyes, and a dollop of orange on their antennae.

Experts at detecting the odor of death, these beetles use their antennae to help them locate small animals within an hour of death from up to two miles away (these beetles specialize in carrion the size of pigeons or small rodents such as prairie dogs or ground squirrels). A breeding pair will get to work right away to prepare the carcass.

If the ground underneath isn't amenable (these beetles strongly prefer soils with high moisture), the beetles will move the carcass to a preferable site for burial. They will loosen the soil, plowing through it from beneath the carcass, eventually causing the carcass to settle into the ground. After covering the carcass with several inches of soil, the beetles clean off any feathers or fur and work the carcass into the shape of a ball. The female will lay eggs in a depression on top of the carcass ball. Burying beetles provide their larvae with parental care, which is uncommon in insects. The adults provide predigested carrion to the larvae on request until they have grown enough to feed themselves. American burying beetles are active at night, which prevents competition with the day-active flies that lay eggs on carcasses; the burying of the carcass also reduces competition. Thus, young burying beetles grow up in a relatively safe environment, and their work breaks down the carrion and adds nutrients to the soil. As the carrion is broken down by the beetles, nitrogen, phosphorus, potassium, sulfur, magnesium, and sodium increase in soils underneath.

Once found in 35 states in the eastern and central United States, American burying beetles are now found only in undisturbed habitats (e.g., prairies, forest edges, and scrubland) in Nebraska, Rhode Island, Oklahoma, South Dakota, Kansas, and Arkansas, along with populations that have been reintroduced in Ohio, Massachusetts, and Missouri. The species was listed as federally endangered in 1989; in 2019, the United States Fish and Wildlife Service proposed reclassifying the beetle as threatened rather than endangered. Causes for the beetle's decline include habitat loss and fragmentation, a reduction of the small mammals and birds on which these beetles grow, and an increase in competition with larger scavengers (e.g., crows, foxes, and raccoons) that compete for available carrion in disturbed areas. Climate change is now also a threat, since these beetles have a limited ability to tolerate warmer temperatures and changes in soil moisture.

FIGURE 10—American burying beetle adult searching for a new burial site.

FIGURE 11—American burying beetle adult digging a new burial site.

FIGURE 12—American burying beetle larvae feeding on a mouse carcass.

Grouping soil organisms based upon their ecological roles is helpful for understanding their function. We do not organize animals that way in this handbook, but throughout the profiles, we describe functional groups where they apply. Here are a few examples of these ecological roles:

- Plant root symbionts (e.g., nitrogen-fixing bacteria and mycorrhizal fungi)
- Decomposers (e.g., bacteria, cellulose- and lignin-degrading fungi, and earthworms)
- Elemental transformers (e.g., denitrifying bacteria)
- Soil engineers (e.g., earthworms, ants, and termites)
- Herbivores and pathogens (e.g., plant-eating nematodes, root rot fungi, and root-feeding beetle larvae)
- System regulators (e.g., predatory insects, predatory nematodes, parasites, and hyperparasites)

However we choose to classify them, soil dwellers represent the most species-rich community of organisms on Earth. In fact, based on some estimates, more than four million species of organisms exist in the soil (excluding plant roots), and yet we know very little about the vast majority of these life forms.

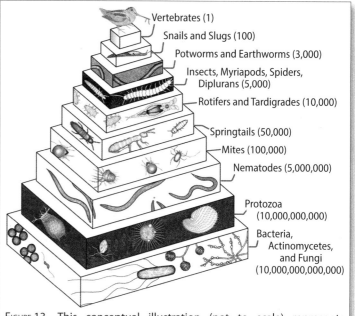

FIGURE 13—This conceptual illustration (not to scale) represents the relative number of individual organisms by group, within one square meter (10.7 square feet) of soil. The most abundant organisms form the base of the pyramid. (Adapted from J. Nardi 2007, Chicago University Press.)

References

Barton, P. S., S. A. Cunningham, D. B. Lindenmayer, and A. D. Manning. 2013. The role of carrion in maintaining biodiversity and ecological processes in terrestrial ecosystems. *Oecologia* 171(4): 761–772.

Carter, D. O., D. Yellowlees, and M. Tibbett. 2007. Cadaver decomposition in terrestrial ecosystems. *Naturwissenschaften* 94(1): 12–24.

Lomolino, M. V., J. C. Creighton, G. D. Schnell, and D. L. Certain. 1995. Ecology and conservation of the endangered American burying beetle (*Nicrophorus americanus*). *Conservation Biology* 9(3): 605–614.

Parmenter, R. R., and J. A. MacMahon. 2009. Carrion decomposition and nutrient cycling in a semiarid shrub–steppe ecosystem. *Ecological Monographs* 79(4): 637–661.

Sikes, D. S., and C. J. Raithel. 2002. A review of hypotheses of decline of the endangered American burying beetle (Silphidae: *Nicrophorus americanus* Olivier). *Journal of Insect Conservation* 6(2): 103–113.

USFWS. 2019. *Reclassifying the American Burying Beetle from Endangered to Threatened on the Federal List of Endangered and Threatened Wildlife. United States Fish and Wildlife Service, Docket number FWS-R2-ES-2018-0029.* Available at: www.federalregister.gov/documents/2019/09/09/2019-19245/endangered-and-threatened-wildlife-and-plants-reclassifying-the-american-burying-beetle-from. Accessed November 2019.

2

Soil Health

Soil is the foundation of all terrestrial life, including humans. This includes the life generated by both wild soils, such as forests and grasslands, and by the agricultural soils that are the focus of this handbook. Given this, it's natural to be interested in the health of our soils, and indeed people often talk about soil health. But what does soil health even mean?

If you're reading this, we're guessing you've had many of the same experiences that we've had with soil. For example, think of a time when you dug into a soil that was rich, loose, and earthy smelling, with fine bits of soft organic matter and probably a few bugs, and that seemed to exhale into your hand. Now in contrast, remember a moment when you tried digging into a soil that was hard, dry, pale, compacted, and sparsely covered with plants, other than maybe a few tough weeds. It's obvious which of those soils was healthy, even if we can't immediately describe the exact scientific properties that each soil possessed. All of us have a natural intuition that can help us evaluate the aliveness of different soils. This sense of aliveness is a good starting point in discussing the concept of soil health, especially if we are focused on the soils that grow crops and feed us.

FIGURE 14—For this soil in South Dakota, the practices of no-till, cover crops and a diverse crop rotation of corn-corn-pea-wheat-soy (pictured) have increased the amount of organic matter, soil organisms and healthy soil function.

Beyond simple intuition, one technical definition of soil health might be this: soil health is the degree to which a soil is optimized to support various ecosystem services (such as crop production, water infiltration, and carbon sequestration). In their article from 2000, John Doran and Michael Zeiss define soil health as "the capacity of soil to function as a vital living system, within ecosystem and land-use boundaries, to sustain plant and animal productivity, maintain or enhance water and air quality, and promote plant and animal health." One regenerative farmer that Xerces has worked with in the midwestern United States has told us that he recognizes healthy soil when he has been able to decrease external inputs while maintaining good and stable crop yields.

As we noted earlier, soils have chemical, physical, and biological properties. In some cases in agricultural landscapes, alteration of these properties may increase or optimize various functions. In other cases, alteration may degrade soil properties, hindering important functions.

Plants, soil animals, and microbial nutrient cycling, through their aliveness, capture carbon from the atmosphere and hold it in their cells. This is carbon sequestration, a key function of healthy soils and of vital importance to balancing carbon dioxide, a greenhouse gas that contributes to global climate change. In the face of our present situation, a new soil health paradigm would focus on creating new soil and restoring the life in it.

Soil Health and Crop Yields

Research demonstrates that farm practices that improve soil health provide numerous agronomic benefits. For example, some studies demonstrate that natural sources of fertilizer, such as manure and green manure, can sustain long-term crop yields. One 2011 study from the Rodale Institute compared the long-term yield potential of organic inputs versus conventional synthetic-input-based soil management over a 22-year period in Pennsylvania. Throughout this study, researchers found that crop yields between the two systems were comparable under normal conditions. However, under drought conditions, corn yields were roughly one-third greater in the organic-input plots due to the increased water-holding capacity of those soils (resulting from higher levels of soil organic matter). Moreover, the overall costs associated with the organic plots were also 15% lower than their conventional counterparts.

FIGURE 15—Cover cropping is a soil conservation practice that also provides habitat for soil organisms and can be adapted for use in orchard crops as well as field crops.

"Land, then, *is not merely soil;* it is a fountain of energy flowing through a circuit of soils, plants and animals.

Food chains are the living channels which conduct energy upward; death and decay return it to the soil.

The circuit is not closed; some energy is dissipated in decay, some is added by absorption from the air, some is stored in soils, peats and long-lived forests; but *it is a sustained circuit, like a slowly augmented revolving fund of life."*

– Aldo Leopold, *A Sand County Almanac and Sketches Here and There*, 1949.

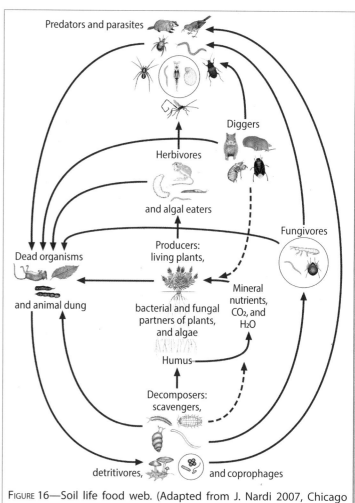

FIGURE 16—Soil life food web. (Adapted from J. Nardi 2007, Chicago University Press.)

Dung Beetles

Humans have long been fascinated by dung beetles (family Geotrupidae and subfamilies Scarabaeinae and Aphodiinae of family Scarabaeidae). Prominent in ancient Egyptian mythology, dung beetles were associated with rebirth after death and were considered sacred. Ancient Greeks and Romans adopted the scarab as a good luck symbol, and images of a beetle and its dung ball even appeared on ancient coins. In most cultures today, dung beetles are valued for their efficient cleanup activities.

Dung beetles are adept at locating dung, a resource for which there is a great deal of competition. In order to minimize competition with flies that may lay their eggs in the dung, dung beetles will slice off a chunk of dung, maneuver it into a ball, and bury it, sometimes relocating it before burial. An egg is laid on each ball of dung, and larvae consume the dung after emerging, digesting the cellulose in the dung's plant material with the help of gut microbes. The burial of dung and the excavation of chambers for young dung beetles influences soil physically and chemically. Dung beetles mix nutrients from dung with the soil, help reduce soil compaction, and help facilitate the further breakdown of the dung by microorganisms.

Dung beetles are present in many landscapes, but their activity in rangelands is the most studied because of their benefits to producers. Dung beetles accelerate the incorporation of dung into soil, and they increase plant productivity of rangelands. Cattle dung contains undigested plant materials. When deposited on the soil surface, dung smothers plant growth in the immediate vicinity, and forage around it is often unused by cattle until the dung is broken down. When left on the soil surface, nutrients like phosphorus, potassium, or nitrogen can be lost to leaching, runoff, or volatilization, reducing nutrient availability to plants. In grazing systems where antiparasitic treatments for cattle are present in dung, it can take up to three years longer or more for dung pats to degrade than when treatments are absent because the antiparasitic compounds are toxic to many invertebrates, including dung beetles.

In addition to their contributions to nutrient cycling and plant growth, dung beetles, along with predatory beetles, such as rove and hister beetles, help suppress dung-inhabiting pests and parasites of cattle and other grazers, such as horn flies (*Haematobia irritans*). Dung beetles also act as secondary seed dispersers, moving seeds that are present in dung. On farmlands, dung beetles reduce food-borne pathogens such as *E. coli* up to 90%, supporting food safety. Although not revered to the extent as they were thousands of years ago, dung beetles continue to provide essential services to us and for their natural communities.

FIGURE 17—Dung beetle (*Canthon* sp.).

FIGURE 18—A male dung beetle rolls a ball of cow dung and presents it to the female beetle (top). Then the pair roll the ball (bottom) to bury it, mate and lay eggs.

Soil Health and Downstream Impacts

Beyond direct benefits at the farm level, the ways we manage soils and the things we add to soils have far-reaching implications and impacts:

- Runoff from fields where plant nutrients have been applied can lead to impaired water quality. Phosphorus in runoff is a contributing factor to freshwater eutrophication, a process that promotes the growth of cyanobacteria and algae, and results in depleted oxygen levels and a buildup of toxins in those waters. Nitrogen that leaves agricultural fields is the primary cause of large-scale oceanic dead zones where rivers empty into oceans.

- Contamination of nitrogen-rich fertilizers in groundwater can directly impact human health, especially in infants in the form of acquired methemoglobinemia (also known as blue baby syndrome).

- The long-term use of synthetic fertilizers can contribute to soil acidification and the accumulation of soil salts and toxic metals.

- The annual production of synthetic nitrogen fertilizer requires billions of cubic feet of natural gas. The resulting greenhouse gas byproducts have massive implications for climate change. Research conducted in the United Kingdom suggests that two kilograms of carbon dioxide are generated for every kilogram of ammonium nitrate fertilizer produced. Moreover, the conversion of nitrate, that is either soil- or fertilizer-derived, to nitrous oxide (such as by soil bacteria) produces an additional greenhouse gas that adds to atmospheric warming.

- Soil health and soil conservation also have economic implications. One study found that for every dollar spent on soil conservation at the farm level, 5–10× that amount can be saved in associated downstream costs, such as river dredging and flood control.

FIGURE 19—Flooding and runoff is one cause of soil erosion that contributes to a loss of soil function and decreased water quality downstream.

FIGURE 20—Integrating livestock with crop production enhances nutrient cycling, helps to build soil organic matter, manages weeds and diversifies the food webs of soil invertebrates.

Soil Health and Soil Life

The number and diversity of living things in soil are typically considered important indicators of soil health. This biological richness can most obviously be observed in natural soils, such as wild grassland and forest soils.

In contrast, intensive cultivation and overgrazing can reduce the aliveness of soil. One example of this was clearly demonstrated in a survey of soil organisms conducted across Europe, published in 2015 in Global Change Biology, comparing high-intensity (annual crops and annual tillage) and low-intensity (perennial vegetation without tillage) farming systems. Consistently, the researchers found that high-intensity farming resulted in fewer earthworms, springtails, and oribatid mites (all widely different and diverse animals). As **Chapter 6** of this guide demonstrates, these and other animals perform important functions in the soil and are worthy of conservation. Moreover, we're fortunate to have farming systems and conservation practices that can lower our negative impact on soil and help maintain and enhance the populations of these animals.

....

References

Barbero, E., C. Palestrini, and A. Rolando. 1999. Dung beetle conservation: effects of habitat and resource selection (Coleoptera: Scarabaeoidea). *Journal of Insect Conservation* 3(2): 75–84.

Doran, J. W., and M. R. Zeiss. 2000. Soil health and sustainability: managing the biotic component of soil quality. *Applied Soil Ecology* 15(1): 3–11.

Jones, M. S., Z. Fu, J. P. Reganold, D. S. Karp, T. E. Besser, J. M. Tylianakis, and W. E. Snyder. 2019. Organic farming promotes biotic resistance to foodborne human pathogens. *Journal of Applied Ecology* 56(5): 1117–1127.

Maldonado, M. B., J. N. Aranibar, A. M. Serrano, N. P. Chacoff, and D. P. Vázquez. 2019. Dung beetles and nutrient cycling in a dryland environment. *Catena* 179: 66–73.

Montgomery, D. 2007. *Dirt: The Erosion of Civilizations*. University of California Press. Berkeley, CA.

Omonode, R. A., D. R. Smith, A. Gál, and T. J. Vyn. 2011. Soil Nitrous Oxide Emissions in Corn following Three Decades of Tillage and Rotation Treatments. *Soil Science Society of America Journal* 75: 152–163.

Pecenka, J. R., and J. G. Lundgren. 2018. The importance of dung beetles and arthropod communities on degradation of cattle dung pats in eastern South Dakota. *PeerJ* 6:e5220. doi:10.7717/peerj.5220

Ratcliffe, B. 2006. Scarab beetles in human culture. *Coleopterists Society Monograph* 5: 85–101.

Rodale Institute. 2011. *The Farming Systems Trial: Celebrating 30 Years*. Rodale Institute, Kurtztown PA.

Sands, B., and R. Wall. 2018. Sustained parasiticide use in cattle farming affects dung beetle functional assemblages. *Agriculture, Ecosystems & Environment* 265: 226–235.

Tsiafouli, M. A., E. Thébault, S. P. Sgardelis, P. C. de Ruiter, W. H. van der Putten, K. Birkhofer, L. Hemerik, F. T. de Vries, R. D. Bardgett, M. V. Brady, L. Bjornlund, H. B. Jørgensen, S. Christensen, T. D. Hertefeldt, S. Hotes, W. H. Gera Hol, J. Frouz, M. Liiri, S. R. Mortimer, H. Setälä, J. Tzanopoulos, K. Uteseny, V. Pižl, J. Stary, V. Wolters, and K. Hedlund. 2015, Intensive agriculture reduces soil biodiversity across Europe. *Global Change Biology* 21: 973–985.

Vitousek, P., et al. 1997. Human alteration of the global nitrogen cycle: causes and consequences. *Ecological Applications* 7: 737–750.

Van Grinsven, H. J. M., H. F. M. Ten Berge, T. Dalgaard, B. Fraters, P. Durand, A. Hart, G. Hofman, B. H. Jacobsen, S. T. J. Lalor, J. P. Lesschen, B. Osterburg, K. G. Richards, A. Techen, F. Vertes, J. Webb, and W. J. Willems. 2012. Management, regulation and environmental impacts of nitrogen fertilization in northwestern Europe under the Nitrates Directive; a benchmark study. *Biogeosciences* 9: 5143–5160.

Wood, S., and A. Cowie. 2004. *A Review of Greenhouse Gas Emission Factors for Fertiliser Production*. Research and Development Division, State Forests of New South Wales. Cooperative Research Centre for Greenhouse Accounting. For IEA Bioenergy Task 38.

3

Observing Soil Life

As both the understanding of soil as a living system and the interest in improving soil health increase, the need to reliably evaluate soil health is becoming more apparent. Observation and measurement can help track changes at the same location, allowing you to, for example, compare baseline conditions with conditions present after a few seasons of farming using practices aimed at increasing soil biodiversity. In addition, it may be useful to compare soil health between fields where management methods differ, such as in the use of tillage, cover crops, nutrient or grazing management, or crop rotations.

There are many possible measures of soil health, ranging from biological indicators like the abundance and diversity of soil organisms to various chemical and physical soil characteristics. No single indicator captures all soil functions, and using multiple indicators provides a more complete picture of soil health.

Figure 21—In order to observe soil and soil life, it is usually necessary to disturb the soil. Many valuable observations can be made by keeping the soil as intact as possible.

Because soil is a living, connected matrix with physical structure, roots, channels, and moisture, temperature, and light gradients, the most accurate and meaningful way to measure soil health is to keep the soil sample as intact as possible. The best way to do this is to make direct assessments in the field. Improvement in real soil function can only be measured when the soil ecosystem in its natural state is included in the assessment. It can be helpful to evaluate unmanaged soil of the same type that has a long history of not being disturbed, such as soil that exists in a fencerow or field border. This can provide an idea of the potential for soil health improvement. This chapter outlines several soil health assessment methods that you can use in the field. Since this isn't always possible, we also include methods for lab testing.

On-Farm Observations of Organisms

Soil organisms provide a biological indication of soil health and provide a sense of how complete and complex a soil community is—which top predators, prey, herbivores, and other functional groups are present and in what proportions. One way to measure changes in soil health and function is to begin by collecting and counting these groups at a baseline point in time, continue doing so for several seasons or years after you implement soil health management practices, and then compare the results. The methods here—using pitfall traps or performing Berlese funnel surveys—can be followed with handmade equipment and traps.

Pitfall Traps

A pitfall trap catches animals, mostly invertebrate macrofauna, that move across the soil surface. Follow these steps to construct and use a pitfall trap:

1. Think about timing. Pitfall traps should be used during the growing season when soil animals are most active. Avoid days when rain is likely because rainwater can fill up and overflow the traps, making them temporarily ineffective.

2. Choose the sampling sites. You could choose sampling sites at the same location to establish a baseline (before changes in soil-management practices) and measure changes after you institute beneficial practices, such as no-till methods or cover cropping. To do this, compare the same site at the same time of year under similar weather conditions. You could also choose several sites within the same field at the same time to illustrate the effect of vegetative cover and management practices on the presence and activity of soil animals. To do this, you could place one site in perennial vegetation beyond the field edges; another site in the field, near the edge; and another site in the field far from the edge.

3. Gather the needed supplies. For each site, gather:
   a. A plastic or metal container (e.g., a plastic drinking cup or a yogurt container) that is approximately 4 to 6 in. (10 to 15 cm) in diameter and 3 to 5 in. (8 to 12 cm) deep;
   b. Water or killing preservative,* such as ethanol (70%) and glycerol (30%), to nearly fill the container;
   c. A cover, such as a plastic plate, that is several inches wider than the container in order to exclude rain and other falling debris;
   d. Wire stakes and duct tape to attach the cover;
   e. Tools to dig a pit for the container; and
   f. Flags, ribbon, or other marking to relocate the trap after a sampling period.

4. At each sampling site, dig a small hole in the soil the size of the container. Place the container in the hole, with the top of the container even with the soil surface. Fill the container with a few inches of the killing preservative. Using wire stakes, place the cover over the container but elevated a few inches above the soil surface. Mark with flags.

5. Return after 24 hours, or two or three days, depending on weather, temperature, and the activity of soil animals. Remove the traps. Collect the contents of the container, rinse them with water, dry, identify, and count. Record the results—the number of insects in each functional group (i.e., predator, decomposer, pest, etc.)—to compare with other locations or after changes in soil health management practices.

ⓘ *For a no-kill method, use a dry, inescapable container as described above, check the trap within 24 hours of setting it, and then empty it and release the soil fauna after recording what you find.*

   📷 See the Xerces guide *Beneficial Insects for Natural Pest Control: Soil Scouting* for template data sheets: https://xerces.org/publications/scouting-guides/beneficial-insects-for-natural-pest-control-soil-scouting

FIGURE 22—A household plastic container can be used to make a simple pitfall trap for catching invertebrates that move across the soil surface.

Berlese Funnel Surveys

Berlese funnels (also known as Tullgren funnels) represent a simplified method of surveying mobile soil-dwelling organisms, especially small arthropods such as mites, springtails, and small insects. In this method, a shallow soil or leaf litter sample is collected and placed under a light. Over a period of days (or hours for small samples and funnels), as the light source warms and dries the soil sample, organisms move away from the light and heat and into a trap below. This can be built from household materials and set up indoors, at the farm, or in an office. Follow these steps to construct and use a Berlese funnel:

1. Collect two standardized soil samples, one from a crop field and one from a nearby control site. Examples of control sites include fallow field borders, forest or hedgerow understories, or other natural landscapes within the farm landscape that are protected from disturbance—and from pesticide runoff and drift, and excess nutrient runoff (e.g., non-grazed or cultivated areas consisting of permanent vegetation). Soil samples should be collected from the top 2 in. (5 cm) of the soil surface and ideally will include some surface thatch, vegetation, or crop debris. To collect samples, use a 16-ounce steel food can with both ends removed (to create a hollow cylinder). Press the can into the soil to a depth of 2 in. (5 cm), extracting a shallow core sample.

2. Place the core samples into plastic funnels of roughly the same diameter, with a hardware cloth screen suspending the core sample above the bottom of the funnel.

3. Support the funnels on small collection jars that fit closely around the funnel (so that specimens cannot escape from any space around the mouths of the collection jars). If desired, the collection jars can be partially filled with rubbing alcohol (ethyl or isopropyl) to demobilize and preserve specimens.

Figure 23—A homemade Berlese funnel. The soil sample is held in an upper container that has an open, narrow base (inverted milk jug) on top of a lower container (jar). Over the course of hours and days, heat and light drive the soil invertebrates away from the light bulb source and into the lower container.

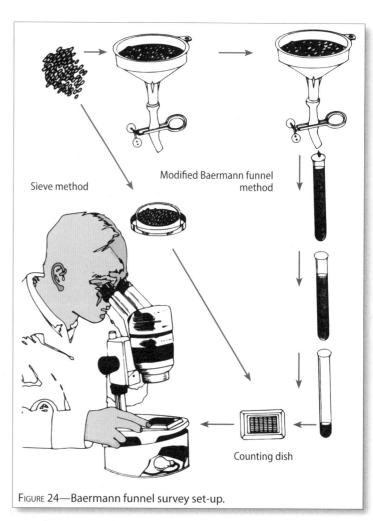

Figure 24—Baermann funnel survey set-up.

4. Finally, suspend a weak heat lamp or incandescent light bulb 3.94–7.87 in. (10–20 cm) above each funnel, and turn it on to slowly warm the soil sample over a 48-to-72-hour period. During this time, soil organisms accustomed to the cool, moist conditions of soil will move lower into the funnel, eventually falling into the collection jar below. Following this extraction period, examine the collected specimens with a standard dissecting microscope at the highest available power. Simple surveys of soil organisms can be conducted using gridded petri dishes.

Baermann Funnel Surveys

Another type of funnel method is the Baermann funnel survey. Baermann funnels are used to collect nematodes from a soil sample using a funnel, paper filter, and water. A dissecting microscope is needed to identify and count the active nematodes from the sample. These funnels can be used to examine other creatures of water films—for example, rotifers, protozoa, and tardigrades.

Field Observations of Soil Characteristics

There are several ways to measure soil characteristics that are relevant to soil health. In-field methods are useful for observing intact, in situ soil function and for comparing before and after management changes. Conventional measures of the physical and chemical properties of soil are relevant to evaluating soil health, but newer methods for measuring biological properties of soil are available or in development. Some examples of in-field measurements are:

- **Plant-available water.** This is much different and more important than water-holding capacity, which is a specific lab test. Plant-available water can be measured with a moisture sensor.
- **Field aggregate stability.** This can be measured with a slake test, described later in this section.
- **Field soil respiration.** This can be measured with a kit. More information is available through the USDA Natural Resources Conservation Service (NRCS): **https://www.nrcs.usda.gov/ Internet/FSE_DOCUMENTS/nrcs142p2_053267.pdf**.
- **Field water infiltration.** This can be demonstrated by pressing a 10-in. (20 cm) section of 5 in. diameter PVC pipe into the soil surface to create a collar that will hold water. Pour a known amount of water into the tube and count the time it takes for the water to infiltrate. Repeat at sites under differing management within the same field or nearby. Compare the times for the water to infiltrate. Shorter infiltration times indicate healthier soil.
- **Habitat for soil organisms.** On the surface and top layer of soil, look for crop and other plant residue. Within a soil profile, look for organic matter, root channels, cavities, or tunnels.

Slake Test

The slake test evaluates the stability of soil aggregates when they are exposed to water. The stability of aggregates in most soils is determined by the soil texture, types of clay, iron content, organic matter, and populations of microbes. The hyphae and spores of arbuscular mycorrhizal fungi living in close association with plant roots produce a range of glue-like proteins. In soils, these proteins produce soil aggregates that are not easily eroded when exposed to rain events or

FIGURE 25—In the slake test demonstration, a soil sample with good aggregate stability (left side) remains intact when suspended in water, while a soil sample with poor aggregate stability falls apart.

flooding. Because more biologically active soils produce more of these natural glues, the slake test provides a convenient process for visually demonstrating the relative microbial richness of soils under different management systems.

To conduct a slake test:

1. Collect two soil aggregates, roughly 2–3 in. (5.1–7.6 cm) in diameter, from a crop field and from a nearby control site. Typical control sites include fallow field borders, forest or hedgerow understories, or other natural landscapes within the farm landscape that are protected from disturbance—and from pesticide runoff and drift, and excess nutrient runoff. Also note: do not collect the crop field aggregate from the plow pan layer of the soil. Focus on the upper 3.94 in. (10 cm) of soil for collection of samples.

2. Allow the soil aggregates to air-dry for 24 to 72 hours until noticeably dry to the touch.

3. Fill two large beakers or glass jars (at least one liter in size) with water and suspend a simple hardware cloth cage in the opening of each beaker. The cage should be suspended underwater and hold the soil aggregate in the upper portion of the beaker.

4. Place each soil aggregate in the hardware cloth cage, ensuring it is fully covered with water. Note that bubbles may appear as water displaces air within the pore spaces of the aggregates.

5. Visually compare each beaker at five minutes, 10 minutes, one hour, and 24 hours. Compare the water clarity between each beaker, the aggregate size, and the amount of sediment that forms at the bottom of each beaker.

Because the slake test is a qualitative visual evaluation, it is not necessary to record data or perform additional measurements. In most cases, immediate and obvious differences between aggregate stability will occur, with intensively farmed soils producing cloudy water and eroded soil aggregates in a very short period of time.

Lab Tests

A handful of lab tests have been developed to quantify some of the components that contribute to soil health. This is an area of soil health that is dynamic and not yet solidified. Like any assessment, these are snapshots and can be best applied to establish a baseline of data and then collect the same information at later times, following management regimes. Lab test results can compare the effects of practices intended to foster soil health. Here are some of the tests:

- **Soil organic matter (SOM).** This cannot be directly measured, but is estimated by combining measures of soil organic carbon, total soil carbon, and the weight lost through ignition.

- **Protein, potentially mineralizable nitrogen (PMN), and phospholipid fatty acids (PLFA).** These tests measure organic compounds that are characteristic of bacteria and fungi and provide an estimate of microbial presence, abundance, and activity.

- **Aggregate stability.** There are wet and dry versions of this test, which measures how well soil aggregates hold together under simulated erosive forces of water or wind.

- **Bulk density.** Bulk density is measured as the dry mass of soil divided by the volume and reflects the porosity, which is influenced by soil life and management practices.

- **Respiration.** This is a measure of the metabolic activity of the soil microbial community, also referred to as carbon mineralization. (Labs vary between 24 and 96 hours of incubation time.)

- **Basic USDA Natural Resources Conservation Service (NRCS) soil health test.** This consists of five core measurements: soil organic carbon, active carbon, respiration, aggregate stability, and extractable protein. This is used in conjunction with a complete nutrient analysis that includes micronutrients.

- **Comprehensive assessment of soil health (CASH).** Developed at Cornell University, CASH measures multiple biological, physical, and chemical indicators. This includes the active carbon (Active C) protocol. Active carbon cycles faster than more recalcitrant forms and might indicate microbial activity. CASH results are presented in table format with ratings.

- Other package soil health tests are Earth Fort and VitTellus.

Comprehensive Assessment of Soil Health

From the Cornell Soil Health Laboratory, Department of Soil and Crop Sciences, School of Integrative Plant Science, Cornell University, Ithaca, NY 14853. http://soilhealth.cals.cornell.edu

Grower:
Mr. T Organic Grains
556 Loamy Haven
Hardwork, PA 12435

Agricultural Service Provider:
Mr. Bob Consulting

Sample ID:	LL6
Field ID:	Deep six
Date Sampled:	10/16/2015
Crops Grown:	COG/COG/COG
Tillage:	more than 9 inches

Test Report

Measured Soil Textural Class: sandy loam

Sand: 59% - Silt: 36% - Clay: 5%

Group	Indicator	Value	Rating	Constraints
physical	Available Water Capacity	0.09	28	
physical	Surface Hardness	255	14	Rooting, Water Transmission
physical	Subsurface Hardness	400	18	Subsurface Pan/Deep Compaction, Deep Rooting, Water and Nutrient Access
physical	Aggregate Stability	56.4	76	
biological	Organic Matter	2.1	54	
biological	ACE Soil Protein Index	6.9	44	
biological	Soil Respiration	0.6	55	
biological	Active Carbon	359	32	
chemical	Soil pH	5.9	54	
chemical	Extractable Phosphorus	2.3	66	
chemical	Extractable Potassium	175.3	100	
chemical	Minor Elements Mg: 134.0 / Fe: 3.4 / Mn: 2.7 / Zn: 1.3		100	

Overall Quality Score: **53** / Medium

FIGURE 26—Example CASH test results.

How to collect samples for lab tests:

- Accurately record location coordinates with GPS and field mark the sampling sites so that you can return to the same point and collect composite samples around the marked point.
- Gather the soil. Most tests require two to six cups of soil using multiple field subsamples. A tile spade is an ideal tool; round tools (e.g., bulb planter or golf hole cutter) and the associated twisting can interfere with aggregate stability tests.
- Be mindful to avoid cross-contamination as much as possible by cleaning shovels, tools, and hands between samples.
- Keep the sample cold with ice and a cooler in the field, and pack the sample to ensure it stays cold during shipping. The lab may provide shipping materials for this.

Comparisons

The most dramatic comparisons of soil health typically occur in two scenarios: (1) crop fields versus unfarmed, vegetated land, and (2) crop fields managed using long-term, continuous conventional tillage versus crop fields managed under no-till systems. Another comparison includes soil samples taken from (1) long-term monocropped fields versus fields managed under highly diverse crop rotations, and (2) overgrazed pastures versus pastures managed with rotational grazing and fallow rest periods.

Like the slake test, Berlese funnel surveys are most useful to compare the same soil type under different management systems. For example, samples of the same soil type from permanent grassland and nearby crop fields can be compared using the Berlese technique to contrast basic richness and abundance of soil organisms. Note that multiple ongoing replications of the slake test and the Berlese funnel technique can be used as a sampling protocol for more robust research projects; however, in the case of this guide, these tests are presented as simplified demonstration projects.

So far, it is not possible to make specific management recommendations (such as which cover crop species to use) based on soil health test results, but certain results would indicate following general beneficial management practices (such as using cover crops), discussed in **Chapter 5**. It isn't yet possible to say, for instance, "If a pitfall trap catches X number of tiger beetles in a 24-hour period, the soil is healthy"—no biological thresholds have been determined. Instead, soil invertebrates can be grouped in functional categories, such as generalist predators or decomposers, and the diversity and abundance of each group compared before, during, and after changes to management practices. For example, in a 2008–2013 study of cover cropping systems by Purdue University researchers, soil health tests showed significant differences between conventional and no-till farming methods, but the tests did not detect differences among the various conservation treatments (such as cover crop species or type of no-till method) within no-till farming.

Keep in mind these important points when testing and comparing results:

- Pick a lab and continue to use that lab. Differences in equipment and techniques can affect the results, making accurate comparisons between tests impossible. This is very important.
- Use laboratories that have enrolled in the North American Proficiency Testing program. This program provides quality assurance and control for many laboratory tests, including the NRCS basic soil health test.
- Different testing labs use different units (either ng/g or nmol/g) for phospholipid-derived fatty acid (PLFA) measurements. To be able to compare results, use labs or tests with the same units.
- Measurable changes in soil health are not immediate. Allow for three years (or even five years) between tests in order to compare the effect of implementing practices that support soil health.
- There is not yet enough understanding of soil health and soil health tests to be able to set a threshold or range for what might constitute a "good" result. The best way to know if a result is good is to compare results between similar soils, cropping systems, and climate.

- CASH ratings are weighted, so each test isn't an equal component to overall rating.
- Results are only a snapshot in time.

....

References

Brown, G. R., and I. M. Matthews. 2016. A review of extensive variation in the design of pitfall traps and a proposal for a standard pitfall trap design for monitoring ground-active arthropod biodiversity. *Ecology and Evolution*, 6: 3953-3964. doi:10.1002/ece3.2176.

Conservation Cropping Systems Initiative, Summary Report—Farmer Sites 2017. https://drive.google.com/file/d/1ZeTcUUQMds5M7cR4F_v-ZCMjfjTBHOWX/view.

Moebius-Clune, B. N., D. J. Moebius-Clune, B. K. Gugino, O. J. Idowu, R. R. Schindelbeck, A. J. Ristow, H. M. van Es, J. E. Thies, H. A. Shayler, M. B. McBride, K. S. M. Kurtz, D. W. Wolfe, and G. S. Abawi. 2016. *Comprehensive Assessment of Soil Health – The Cornell Framework, Edition 3.2*, Cornell University, Geneva, NY. www.css.cornell.edu/extension/soil-health/manual.pdf.

Nimmo, J. R., and K. S. Perkins. 2018. 2.6 Aggregate Stability and Size Distribution. In *Methods of Soil Analysis* (eds J. H. Dane and G. Clarke Topp). doi:10.2136/sssabookser5.4.c14.

Purdue University Extension, *How to understand and interpret soil health tests.* www.extension.purdue.edu/extmedia/AY/AY-366-W.pdf.

Sullivan, D., A. Moore, and L. Brewer. 2019. *Soil organic matter as a soil health indicator: sampling, testing, and interpretation.* https://catalog.extension.oregonstate.edu/sites/catalog/files/project/pdf/em9251.pdf.

Tabatabai, M. A. 1996. Soil organic matter testing: An overview. In *Soil Organic Matter: Analysis and Interpretation* (pp. 1–9). Magdoff, F. R., M. A. Tabatabai, and E. A. Hanlon, Jr. (eds.). Special Publication 46, Soil Science Society of America.

van Es, H., R. Schindelbeck, A. Ristow, K. Kurtz, and L. Fennell. 2017. *Add-on Test: Potentially Mineralizable Nitrogen. Soil Health Manual Series Fact Sheet Number 16-15.* Cornell University Soil Health Laboratory. https://cpb-us-e1.wpmucdn.com/blogs.cornell.edu/dist/f/5772/files/2016/12/15_Potentially_Mineralizable_N_Factsheet-040517-206ld27.pdf.

Weil, R., K. Islam, M. Stine, J. Gruver, and S. Samson-Liebig. 2003. Estimating active carbon for soil quality assessment: A simplified method for laboratory and field use. *American Journal of Alternative Agriculture*, 18(1), 3-17. doi:10.1079/AJAA200228.

Yin, R., J. Siebert, N. Eisenhauer, and M. Schädler. 2020. Climate change and intensive land use reduce soil animal biomass via dissimilar pathways. eLife, 9, e54749. https://doi.org/10.7554/eLife.54749.

4

Farming Practices That Can Put Soil Health at Risk

As a geological and biological matrix, healthy, living soil is protected and buffered against dynamic changes or degradation. However, physical or chemical disruption of the soil environment destroys the healthy function between minerals, water, gases, roots, and animals. Landslides, floods, and storms are naturally occurring disruptions to soils. Many conventional practices used in growing crops are damaging to soil health—in the short term and long term. External inputs or additional disturbance only mask the damage temporarily and are economically and ecologically costly. This chapter describes the negative effects on soil health caused by tillage, climate change, synthetic fertilizer applications, and pesticides. <u>Chapter 5</u> covers practices that can build and protect soils that are healthy and alive.

Tillage

Tillage is destructive to the physical structure of soil and the living organisms within it. The primary reasons for tillage have been to destroy weeds and to achieve consistent planting conditions, but much more is destroyed in the process. The physical disturbance of tillage breaks up soil structure and destroys aggregates and soil pores. (Inversion tillage is the most destructive; plows, disks, shanks, and vertical tillage tools are increasingly less destructive.) Soil structure is critical to water infiltration, root growth, and nutrient and gas exchange. Existing channels from dead roots and earthworm or animal tunnels are lost with tillage. This impacts water infiltration and storage, as well as the habitat value for animals that use the tunnels.

FIGURE 27—Conventional tillage (left) compared with strip tillage (right) of rye.

When surface aggregates are destroyed, the fine particles form a crust that inhibits infiltration and impedes seedling emergence. Tillage churns soil and dramatically increases the exposure of soil surfaces to the atmosphere. This exposes carbon, previously held inside aggregates, to microbes in an oxygen-rich environment. Microbes quickly eat this carbon, and much is lost as carbon dioxide. The loss of soil cover and the exposure of dark soil surfaces to heating by the sun increases soil temperatures. Higher soil temperatures can be detrimental to many soil macrofauna, mesofauna, and microfauna and result in the loss of soil water needed by some animals to move around within the soil.

Tillage results in shifts in detrital food webs: undisturbed soils support extensive fungal networks, and fungi form the basis for detrital food webs in untilled soils, but plowed soils tend to shift toward bacterial decomposers at the base of the detrital food web.

Climate Change

The effect of climate change on soil health and soil organisms depends on a variety of factors, such as geographic region (variable and associated climate change projections), soil type, and land management practices. Most areas in the United States will experience an increase in extreme weather events, including droughts, flooding, and intense storms that can affect soil systems. Many areas, including much of the eastern half of the United States, will experience an increase in extreme rainfall events, which can lead to soil erosion. In the northeastern United States, precipitation intensity and amounts are expected to increase more than most other regions in the United States. In other areas, such as California and the Great Basin, drought will become more common and increasingly unpredictable. Some areas will have increased frequency and duration of flooding. Flooding can scour and wash away soil, and where water sits for days or more, the inundated soils have poor oxygen, which leads to plant and animal death. Increased drought and heat reduce plants' ability to persist, which could leave soils bare and exposed to erosion and result in a cascade of loss of soil animals that depend on plants for food and habitat. The general instability or unpredictability of seasonal temperatures will affect the timing of flowering and life cycles of insects and microbes. Sea level rise will increase the risk of flooding in coastal areas, where inundation with saltwater will be a problem for soil health and farmland productivity.

While climate change can have adverse effects on soil health, especially in systems where soil health is already poor or degraded, soils also have an important role to play in mitigating climate change. Healthy soils sequester more carbon than degraded soils, which means that improving soil health can turn farmland into a climate sink (land that stores more carbon than it releases). Thus, farmers have the potential to lead the fight against climate change—by implementing practices that prioritize soil health, farms become a key part in mitigating the climate crisis. All of the practices described in Chapter 5: <u>Farming Practices that Support Soil Health</u> will improve soil health and improve the carbon sequestration services of soil on your farm.

Synthetic Fertilizers

Inorganic, synthetic fertilizer application creates spikes in the abundance of available nitrogen, phosphorus, and potassium, disrupting the processes of decomposition and nutrient cycling. The response of microbes to the nutrients affects available soil carbon and the diversity and abundance of soil animals. Some groups tend to increase in abundance following nitrogen fertilizer application, such as microbes and animals associated with plant roots and organic matter, while microarthropods decrease. However, long term use of nitrogen fertilizers—particularly ammonium-based N fertilizers—can accelerate soil acidification, which can in turn affect soil microbial communities. Synthetic fertilizers create an imbalance in the natural functioning of soil. USDA soil scientist Rick Haney compares

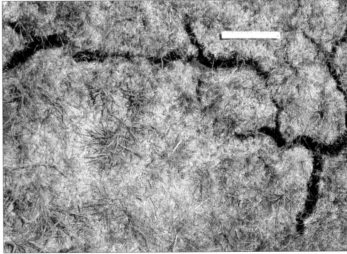

FIGURE 28—Bare soil is subject to erosion by water and wind (top). Soils with higher clay content may crack when dry (bottom).

synthetic fertilizer use to a diet of only vitamins—without fiber (organic matter), the system can't be healthy in the long term. Sustained nutrient cycling and availability depends upon interconnected soil organisms and communities.

Pesticides

Pesticides—which include insecticides, fungicides, herbicides, and soil fumigants—are used to control insects, diseases, weeds, and other pests that can reduce the growth or productivity of agricultural crops. More than one billion pounds of pesticide active ingredients are used annually in the United States, with more than 90% of that usage in agricultural settings.

Impacts of Pesticides on Soil Invertebrates

A variety of pesticides can disrupt soil microbial and invertebrate communities, as well as the soil functions and processes these organisms mediate. Effects of pesticides in soils can range from lethal, including immediate death or shortened life span, to sublethal, such as diminished health, behavior, reproduction, and growth. Pesticides can also affect soil fauna indirectly by disturbing the soil food web and community dynamics (e.g., by reducing prey for natural enemies).

Pesticide residues in soils of crop fields and field margins are a possible route of exposure for the nearly 70% of bee species that nest in soil. Highly mobile systemic insecticides and fungicides move easily from treated fields into the soils and plants of adjacent habitats, including from dust off during the planting of treated seeds as well as movement through soils. (See "Neonicotinoid Insecticides" on page 28 for more information on neonicotinoids, a class of systemic insecticides.) Neonicotinoid residues in the soils of agricultural field margins have been associated with lower richness in bee species visiting those areas. Fungicide contamination could affect larval nutrition and development and make bees more susceptible to other stressors such as insecticide exposure and pathogen infection. Chronic exposure to pesticide residues—for example, bee larvae exposed to contaminated soils—could have a variety of impacts on development, longevity, and reproduction.

Earthworms and potworms, which provide key soil functions and represent the majority of soil faunal biomass in most terrestrial ecosystems, are impacted by pesticides at individual, community, and population levels—some insecticides, fungicides, and herbicides can increase these animals' individual mortality, reduce their growth and reproduction, change individual behavior (such as feeding rate), or decrease the overall community biomass and density. These effects can be mixed and sometimes short-lived, but chronic pesticide exposure in soils is likely to have long-term implications for soil life. Soil communities are likely to exhibit short- and long-term shifts in species composition, favoring soil life that are less susceptible to or that can more readily detoxify pesticides.

A soil organism's degree of exposure to soil pesticides depends on its lifestyle. Soil-dwelling invertebrates that are highly mobile, such as predatory arthropods, are more likely to be exposed as they move through contaminated soils than soil organisms that are fairly stationary. Invertebrates that live close to the soil surface are also more likely to be exposed to pesticides than those that live deeper below the surface.

In the long term, populations and species may adapt in order to survive in contaminated soils, including increasing expression of certain detoxification enzymes. However, these adaptations may come at an unknown energetic, behavioral, or reproductive cost.

It's important to remember that soil invertebrates and the ecological processes they mediate are not the only animals and processes affected by pesticides applied to the soil. Pesticide residues taken up and stored in the tissues of earthworms and other invertebrates can move up food chains, accumulating at higher doses in the birds and other wildlife that eat these soil-dwelling animals. One of the main legacies of the insecticide DDT was its devastating impacts on birds of prey. Modern insecticides, such as neonicotinoids, appear to be having similar cascading negative impacts on insectivorous birds. Pesticide use also poses risks to pesticide applicators, farmworkers, and other communities that are regularly exposed to pesticides. Agricultural workers experience pesticide injury and illness at rates many times higher than the general population, and both acute and chronic exposure to pesticide residues can result in negative health outcomes for farmworkers and their families. Adoption of nonchemical management strategies for insect, disease, and weed management benefits both human health and the environment.

Fate of Pesticides in Soil

Depending on the method and timing of application, some or all of the pesticides applied to crops can end up in the soil. Some pesticides are applied directly to the soil as fumigants, granules, or pellets spread on the soil surface; soil drenches and injections; or seed coatings. Pesticides sprayed on plant foliage or via aerial applications can also move into soil and groundwater; for example, approximately 65% of high-volume sprays applied by ground equipment to blueberry bushes for mite control were found to pass through the bushes into the soil. Pesticides can also enter the soil from crop residues, leaf fall, and root exudates.

Pesticide interactions with soil organic matter and life are complex. Some pesticides bind to soil particles—primarily organic matter—while others may be taken up by plants or leached through the soil profile into water bodies. Adsorption (binding) to soil particles involves a variety of bonding mechanisms and strengths; only some pesticide residues in soil are bioavailable to plants and soil organisms.

Soil microorganisms largely mediate the degradation of pesticides in soil. Bacteria, fungi, algae, and other microbes in the soil metabolize or otherwise catalyze the transformation of pesticide active ingredients into less bioactive substances. At the soil surface, light and heat also work to break down pesticides. Persistence of different pesticides in the soil environment depends on many interacting factors, including climate, soil type, type or nature of the pesticide, and whether it was applied once or several times. Degradation is generally much slower in dry soils.

Soil amendments like compost and manure can affect the fate of pesticides. Increasing organic matter content may increase the adsorptive capacity of soils, as well as microbial activity and associated decomposition of pesticides. Tillage also interacts with pesticide residues in soil—some pesticides are intentionally incorporated into soil through tillage, and in other cases, tillage that brings pesticide residues to the soil surface may lead to volatilization (evaporation of residues into the atmosphere) or degradation of those residues. Pesticides that volatilize can move far from where they were applied as vapor drift before settling back out of the atmosphere.

The NRCS offers a pesticide risk screening tool, Windows Pesticide Screening Tool (WIN-PST). This tool can help evaluate the potential for a pesticide to leach or run off at a site based on the pesticide's physicochemical

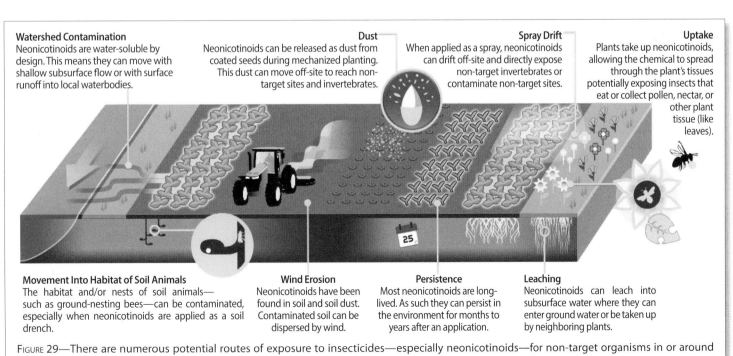

Watershed Contamination
Neonicotinoids are water-soluble by design. This means they can move with shallow subsurface flow or with surface runoff into local waterbodies.

Dust
Neonicotinoids can be released as dust from coated seeds during mechanized planting. This dust can move off-site to reach non-target sites and invertebrates.

Spray Drift
When applied as a spray, neonicotinoids can drift off-site and directly expose non-target invertebrates or contaminate non-target sites.

Uptake
Plants take up neonicotinoids, allowing the chemical to spread through the plant's tissues potentially exposing insects that eat or collect pollen, nectar, or other plant tissue (like leaves).

Movement Into Habitat of Soil Animals
The habitat and/or nests of soil animals—such as ground-nesting bees—can be contaminated, especially when neonicotinoids are applied as a soil drench.

Wind Erosion
Neonicotinoids have been found in soil and soil dust. Contaminated soil can be dispersed by wind.

Persistence
Most neonicotinoids are long-lived. As such they can persist in the environment for months to years after an application.

Leaching
Neonicotinoids can leach into subsurface water where they can enter ground water or be taken up by neighboring plants.

FIGURE 29—There are numerous potential routes of exposure to insecticides—especially neonicotinoids—for non-target organisms in or around agricultural settings.

characteristics and the site's specific conditions, such as soil type and slope. The downloadable WIN-PST database (see Resources) includes a variety of information about the toxicity and environmental fate of currently registered pesticides.

Insecticides

Insecticides, particularly broad-spectrum insecticides with a mode of action affecting many different types of insects, are generally the most toxic pesticides to arthropods in the soil. Broad-spectrum insecticides such as organophosphates, carbamates, avermectins, neonicotinoids, and synthetic pyrethroids can reduce the abundance, species richness, or biomass of predatory arthropods, isopods, earthworms, and potworms in the soil. Insecticides can have complex ripple effects in soil food webs: loss of predators following insecticide applications can result in

Neonicotinoid Insecticides

Neonicotinoids are the most widely used class of insecticides worldwide, representing more than 25% of total global insecticide sales. Neonicotinoids pose a particular risk to soil invertebrate communities due to their high toxicity to most insects, systemic properties, and persistence in soils. Half-lives of the nitro-substituted neonicotinoids (including imidacloprid, thiamethoxam, and clothianidin) range from about five to 25 weeks in soil, with some estimates ranging as high as two to three years. A general rule of thumb is that it takes approximately five half-lives to functionally eliminate a substance from the soil environment.

Neonicotinoid seed treatments can have complex effects on aboveground and belowground invertebrate communities. Only a small proportion (approximately 2–20%) of the active ingredient in neonicotinoid soil or seed treatments is taken up by plants; the bulk of the active ingredient remains in the soil and may pose risks to soil organisms. A meta-analysis of 20 field studies found that neonicotinoid seed treatments and pyrethroid insecticide applications had similar negative impacts on natural enemy abundance, reducing abundance of beneficial insects by an average of 16% compared with untreated fields. Natural enemies—including minute pirate bugs, lady beetles, lacewings, spiders, ground beetles, and rove beetles— were found to be significantly less abundant in surface litter in clothianidin-treated corn plots than untreated plots. Loss of these natural enemies and other soil macrofauna could result in disruptions to the ecosystem services they provide, including controlling insect pests and consuming weed seeds.

Residual imidacloprid in the fallen leaves of treated trees inhibited earthworm and aquatic insect feeding and reduced leaf litter breakdown in two studies. These sublethal effects on decomposers could have broad implications for organic matter breakdown and nutrient cycling in terrestrial and aquatic ecosystems. Agricultural plant litter with imidacloprid residues may have similar feeding inhibition effects on decomposers.

FIGURE 30—Neonicotinoid-treated seeds in a hopper.

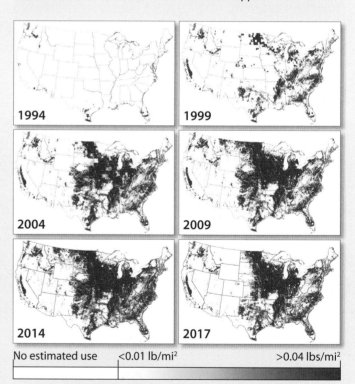

1994   1999
2004   2009
2014   2017

No estimated use   <0.01 lb/mi²   >0.04 lbs/mi²

FIGURE 31—Estimated Annual Agricultural Use of Imidacloprid in the United States: 1994–2017. Source: http://water.usgs.gov/nawqa/pnsp/usage/maps/compound_listing.php

population spikes of their prey. Sometimes these population spikes become secondary pest outbreaks; pests that were previously suppressed by natural enemies reach a population level at which they cause economic damage to crops.

Systemic insecticides, including neonicotinoids, sulfoximines, and anthranilic diamides, are water-soluble pesticides that move easily within plants and can be translocated from the site of application to other parts of the plant. Typically, systemic insecticides are applied to soil and taken up by plant roots, but they can also be applied to foliage or injected directly into woody plants. Because these chemicals dissolve easily in water, they can be quite mobile in soils and prone to leaching and off-site movement. Large-scale use of systemic insecticides in agriculture has raised concern about negative impacts on decomposition, nutrient cycling, soil respiration, and invertebrate populations.

Studies of neonicotinoid seed treatments have found mixed impacts on soil microbial activity and community composition, with some studies indicating that effects of seed treatments are short-term and even stimulatory, and others finding adverse effects on soil microbial communities and their function (e.g., lower respiration rate or metabolic activity, and shifts in community composition or diversity).

Fungicides

While insecticides are the pesticides likely to pose the greatest risk to soil-dwelling arthropods, fungicides may have larger impacts on soil microbial activity. Heavy metal fungicides (e.g., copper, zinc, and sulfur) significantly reduced the biomass, activity, and diversity of earthworms and soil microbial communities in orchard and vineyard soils. Soil and lab experiments have found that copper negatively affects survival and growth of earthworms, and that earthworms tend to avoid or move out of copper-contaminated soils, preferring soils with a lower copper concentration.

Fungicide applications that reduce earthworm abundance or activity may slow the breakdown of leaf litter that these soil fauna provide. Applications of the benzimidazole fungicides benomyl and thiophanate-methyl reduced surface earthworm populations and slowed leaf removal in apple orchards, with some residual effects on earthworm abundance lasting up to three years after benomyl applications.

Herbicides

Herbicides can have direct or indirect effects on soil invertebrates. Some herbicides, including paraquat and 2,4–D, can have direct sublethal or lethal impacts on a variety of beneficial insects, particularly their developing larvae. Glyphosate, the most widely used herbicide in the world, has been found to disrupt earthworm movement and reduce reproduction—although it is not clear whether these effects are due to direct toxicity or simply the loss of plant cover at the soil surface.

In some cases, exposure to herbicides may make invertebrates more susceptible to other pesticides they are exposed to in the soil environment. Triazine herbicides, such as atrazine and simazine, can synergize the toxicity of certain insecticides, particularly organophosphates. Atrazine has been found to increase the toxicity of the organophosphate insecticide chlorpyrifos to invertebrates by several fold. Glyphosate may synergize the effects of insecticide or fungicide seed dressings on earthworm activity.

Some herbicides, including atrazine, simazine, glyphosate, and paraquat, can have a repellent effect on predatory ground beetles, which play important roles for pest and weed seed control in agricultural fields. In one study, beetles did not return to treated fields for a month after application of glyphosate or paraquat. This effect may be a response by these predatory insects to the loss of plant cover in herbicide-treated fields.

Indirect Effects

In general, in agricultural settings, herbicides are used to reduce aboveground plant diversity in favor of monoculture in order to reduce competition with the focal crop. Aboveground plant diversity drives the diversity and abundance of soil organisms—and vice versa—and so the loss of plants due to herbicide use is likely to negatively impact the diversity and abundance of soil-dwelling organisms that feed on pollen, nectar, seeds, leaves, roots, and other plant tissues. Changing organic matter inputs may also affect populations of soil decomposers.

Soil Fumigants

Soil fumigants are pesticides that, when injected or incorporated into soil, form a gas that diffuses through the pockets of air in soils. Fumigants are typically used weeks to months before crop planting to control a broad range of soilborne pests, including insects, nematodes, bacteria, fungi, and weeds. Many fumigants are toxic to a broad spectrum of soil life and will kill beneficial organisms along with soilborne pathogens. The use of fumigants can cause long-term disruption in the balance of soil communities—some organisms are more susceptible to fumigants than others, and some are better able to recolonize soils following fumigation. Interestingly, fumigants are generally far more harmful to mycorrhizal fungi than soil-applied fungicides, and in some cases have led to plant stunting due to elimination of beneficial mycorrhizal fungi in fumigated soils.

Knowledge Gaps

There are major knowledge gaps regarding pesticide impacts on most soil invertebrates and the ecosystem functions they provide and regulate. Many of the pesticides used have toxicity data for fewer than five soil invertebrate species. The current pesticide risk assessment framework in the United States fails to capture the diversity of responses and sensitivity to pesticides among soil invertebrates. The model organism for soil invertebrates that is typically used for lower-tier testing of pesticide toxicity, the red wiggler (*Eisenia fetida*), a habitat specialist earthworm, was chosen mainly for its amenability to laboratory testing rather than for its ecological relevance. Other soil invertebrates, such as springtails (Collembola), may be far more sensitive to pesticides than earthworms.

We also know little about community and population responses of soil invertebrates to the complex mixture of pesticides and their metabolites likely to be present in crop soils. Few studies have examined the interactive effects of different pesticide mixtures (e.g., whether mixtures are additive, synergistic, or antagonistic in their toxicity to soil organisms).

Many pesticides can persist via a variety of binding mechanisms for months to years in the soil. While some residues are biologically inactive once adhered to soil particles, some remain bioavailable or can become bioavailable through interactions with soil microbes. There are few long-term studies examining the effects of chronic low-dose exposure to pesticide residues in the soil, including the metabolites produced as pesticides break down over time.

Recommendations

The first line of defense in managing pests is prevention. There are many cultural, biological, and mechanical methods that can break pest and disease cycles and keep pest populations at tolerable levels, reducing the need for pesticide applications. Use pesticides as a last resort if preventive strategies are not feasible, or if scouting and monitoring determine that pests have reached damaging levels despite preventive management. Do not apply pesticides before knowing if there is a problem. Neonicotinoid and other pesticidal seed treatments are often used without knowing whether the target pests are present or a problem in the fields where they are planted. Prophylactic use of these seed coatings across millions of acres of cropland is a waste of resources and poses a variety of environmental risks.

Scouting and monitoring can help determine what pests are present and whether populations are high enough to result in economic damage to crops. Once you know what's in your fields, you should seek resources on pest life cycles and habitat requirements to figure out the best approaches for keeping their populations low over time. Think of it this way: if you have ants in the kitchen, you'd clean your sink and counters to remove the food sources that are attracting them. The same principle is true for removing food or shelter for insect pests and cleaning up infested plant materials in crop fields.

If you use pesticides, take steps to reduce the risk to soil life:

- Use the principles of integrated pest management to increase prevention-based strategies and reduce reliance on chemical management. Scout and monitor for insect pests and diseases and only apply pesticides if a pest has reached economically damaging levels.

- If using pesticides, target applications to the areas where pests are present. Reduced coverage methods like spot spraying and band or alternate-row applications can reduce pesticide use and cost while maintaining efficacy for a variety of crop pests.
- Do not use soil fumigants, which disrupt the balance and reduce the diversity of soil communities.
- Avoid tank mixing wherever possible, particularly mixes of insecticides, fungicides, or herbicides that are known to jointly increase toxicity when applied together. The University of California IPM Bee Precaution Pesticide Ratings tool (see **Resources**) can help identify some of these synergistic mixtures.
- Choose less persistent and more selective options to reduce impacts on nontarget organisms.
- Minimize drift and off-site movement into natural areas near crop fields. These areas are refuges that allow soil organisms to recolonize crop fields after disturbances like tillage or pesticide applications. Consider use of electrostatic sprayers that improve deposition onto the target plant foliage and therefore reduce the amount of pesticide applied and the amount likely to reach soils.
- Follow all label instructions and apply pesticides at the lowest effective rate and frequency to minimize the amount reaching soils.

References

Anderson, T. D., and M. J. Lydy. 2002. Increased toxicity to invertebrates associated with a mixture of atrazine and organophosphate insecticides. *Environmental Toxicology and Chemistry* / SETAC 21: 1507–1514.

Atwood, D., and C. Paisley-Jones. 2017. *Pesticides industry sales and usage: 2008–2012 Market Estimates*. Washington, DC: US Environmental Protection Agency.

Atwood, L. W., D. A. Mortensen, R. T. Koide, and R. G. Smith. 2018. Evidence for multi-trophic effects of pesticide seed treatments on non-targeted soil fauna. *Soil Biology & Biochemistry* 125: 144–155.

Bass, C., I. Denholm, M. S. Williamson, and R. Nauen. 2015. The global status of insect resistance to neonicotinoid insecticides. *Pesticide Biochemistry and Physiology* 121: 78–87.

Bromilow, R. H., A. A. Evans, P. H. Nicholls, A. D. Todd, G. G. Briggs. 1996. The effect on soil fertility of repeated applications of pesticides over 20 years. *Pest Management Science* 48: 63–72.

Brust, G. E. 1990. Direct and indirect effects of four herbicides on the activity of carabid beetles (Coleoptera: Carabidae). *Pesticide Science* 30: 309–320.

Bünemann, E. K., G. D. Schwenke, and L. Van Zwieten. 2006. Impact of agricultural inputs on soil organisms—a review. *Australian Journal of Soil Research* 44: 379–406.

Chagnon, M., D. Kreutzweiser, E. A. D. Mitchell, C. A. Morrissey, D. A. Noome, and J. P. Van der Sluijs. 2015. Risks of large-scale use of systemic insecticides to ecosystem functioning and services. *Environmental Science and Pollution Research International* 22: 119–134.

Coats, J. R. 1991. Pesticide degradation mechanisms and environmental activation. Pages 10–30 *Pesticide Transformation Products*. American Chemical Society.

Cook, M. E., and A. A. J. Swait. 1975. Effects of some fungicide treatments on earthworm populations and leaf removal in apple orchards. *The Journal of Horticultural Science* 50: 495–499.

Cox, L., P. Velarde, A. Cabrera, M. C. Hermosín, and J. Cornejo. 2007. Dissolved organic carbon interactions with sorption and leaching of diuron in organic-amended soils. *European Journal of Soil Science* 58: 714–721.

DiBartolomeis, M., S. Kegley, P. Mineau, R. Radford, and K. Klein. 2019. An assessment of acute insecticide toxicity loading (AITL) of chemical pesticides used on agricultural land in the United States. *PloS One* 14: e0220029.

Disque, H. H., K. A. Hamby, A. Dubey, C. Taylor, and G. P. Dively. 2019. Effects of clothianidin-treated seed on the arthropod community in a mid-Atlantic no-till corn agroecosystem. *Pest Management Science* 75: 969–978.

Edwards, C. A., and D. Pimentel. 1989. Impact of herbicides on soil ecosystems. *Critical Reviews in Plant Sciences* 8: 221–257.

Eijsackers, H., P. Beneke, M. Maboeta, J. P. E. Louw, and A. J. Reinecke. 2005. The implications of copper fungicide usage in vineyards for earthworm activity and resulting sustainable soil quality. *Ecotoxicology and Environmental Safety* 62: 99–111.

Enders, L. S., L. C. Rault, T. M. Heng-Moss, B. D. Siegfried, and N. J. Miller. 2019. Transcriptional responses of soybean aphids to sublethal insecticide exposure. *Insect Biochemistry and Molecular Biology* 118: 103285.

Fierer, N., M. S. Strickland, D. Liptzin, M. A. Bradford, and C. C. Cleveland. 2009. Global patterns in belowground communities. *Ecology Letters* 12: 1238–1249.

Frampton, G. K., and P. J. van den Brink. 2007. Collembola and macroarthropod community responses to carbamate, organophosphate and synthetic pyrethroid insecticides: direct and indirect effects. *Environmental Pollution* 147: 14–25.

Frampton, G. K., S. Jansch, J. J. Scott-Fordsmand, J. Römbke, and P. J. Van den Brink. 2006. Effects of pesticides on soil invertebrates in laboratory studies: a review and analysis using species sensitivity distributions. *Environmental Toxicology and Chemistry* / SETAC 25: 2480–2489.

Freydier, L., and J. G. Lundgren. 2016. Unintended effects of the herbicides 2,4-D and dicamba on lady beetles. *Ecotoxicology* 25: 1270–1277.

Gaupp-Berghausen, M., M. Hofer, B. Rewald, and J. G. Zaller. 2015. Glyphosate-based herbicides reduce the activity and reproduction of earthworms and lead to increased soil nutrient concentrations. *Scientific Reports* 5: 12886.

Gevao, B., K. T. Semple, and K. C. Jones. 2000. Bound pesticide residues in soils: a review. *Environmental Pollution* 108: 3–14.

Goulson, D. 2013. An overview of the environmental risks posed by neonicotinoid insecticides. *Journal of Applied Ecology* 50: 977–987.

Hallmann, C. A., R. P. B. Foppen, C. A. M. van Turnhout, H. de Kroon, and E. Jongejans. 2014. Declines in insectivorous birds are associated with high neonicotinoid concentrations. *Nature* 511: 341–343.

James, R. L. 1989. Effects of fumigation on soil pathogens and beneficial microorganisms. *Proceedings of the Intermountain Forest Nursery Association*. USDA, Bismark, ND: 29–34.

Jänsch, S., G. K. Frampton, J. Römbke, P. J. Van den Brink, and J. J. Scott-Fordsmand. 2006. Effects of pesticides on soil invertebrates in model ecosystem and field studies: a review and comparison with laboratory toxicity data. *Environmental Toxicology and Chemistry / SETAC* 25: 2490–2501.

Jones, A., P. Harrington, and G. Turnbull. 2014. Neonicotinoid concentrations in arable soils after seed treatment applications in preceding years. *Pest Management Science* 70: 1780–1784.

Kolar, L., N. Kozuh Erzen, L. Hogerwerf, and C. A. M. van Gestel. 2008. Toxicity of abamectin and doramectin to soil invertebrates. *Environmental Pollution* 151: 182–189.

Kreutzweiser, D. P., K. P. Good, D. T. Chartrand, T. A. Scarr, and D. G. Thompson. 2008. Are leaves that fall from imidacloprid-treated maple trees to control Asian longhorned beetles toxic to non-target decomposer organisms? *Journal of Environmental Quality* 37: 639–646.

Kreutzweiser, D. P., D. G. Thompson, and T. A. Scarr. 2009. Imidacloprid in leaves from systemically treated trees may inhibit litter breakdown by non-target invertebrates. *Ecotoxicology and Environmental Safety* 72: 1053–1057.

Lu, C., R. A. Fenske, N. J. Simcox, and D. Kalman. 2000. Pesticide exposure of children in an agricultural community: evidence of household proximity to farmland and take home exposure pathways. *Environmental Research* 84(3): 290–302. https://doi.org/10.1006/enrs.2000.4076.

Mäder, P., A. Fliessbach, D. Dubois, L. Gunst, P. Fried, and U. Niggli. 2002. Soil fertility and biodiversity in organic farming. *Science* 296: 1694–1697.

Main, A. R., E. B. Webb, K. W. Goyne, and D. Mengel. 2020. Reduced species richness of native bees in field margins associated with neonicotinoid concentrations in non-target soils. *Agriculture, Ecosystems & Environment* 287: 106693.

Menge, J. A. 1982. Effect of soil fumigants and fungicides on vesicular-arbuscular fungi. *Phytopathology* 72: 1125–1133.

Merrington, G., S. L. Rogers, and L. Van Zwieten. 2002. The potential impact of long-term copper fungicide usage on soil microbial biomass and microbial activity in an avocado orchard. *Australian Journal of Soil Research* 40: 749–759.

Morton, H. L., and J. O. Moffett. 1972. Ovicidal and larvicidal effects of certain herbicides on honey bees. *Environmental Entomology* 1: 611–614.

Morton, H. L., J. O. Moffett, and R. H. Macdonald. 1972. Toxicity of herbicides to newly emerged honey bees. *Environmental Entomology* 1: 102–104.

Mustapha, M., N. Halimoon, W. L. Wan Johari, and M. Abd Shakur. 2018. Soil microorganisms and their potential in pesticide biodegradation: A review. *Journal of Sustainable Agricultural Sciences* 44: 39–61.

Paoletti, M. G., E. Iovane, and M. Cortese. 1988. Pedofauna bioindicators and heavy metals in five agroecosystems in north-east Italy. *Revue d'Ecologie et de Biologie du Sol* 25: 33–58.

Paoletti, M. G., D. Sommaggio, M. R. Favretto, G. Petruzzelli, B. Pezzarossa, and M. Barbafieri. 1998. Earthworms as useful bioindicators of agroecosystem sustainability in orchards and vineyards with different inputs. *Agriculture, Ecosystems & Environment* 10: 137–150.

Pimentel, D., and L. Levitan. 1986. Pesticides: Amounts applied and amounts reaching pests. *Bioscience* 36: 86–91.

Russell, C., and C. B. Schultz. 2009. Effects of grass-specific herbicides on butterflies: an experimental investigation to advance conservation efforts. *Journal of Insect Conservation* 14: 53–63.

Schiffman, R. 2017. *Why it's time to stop punishing our soils with fertilizers. Yale E360*. Yale School of Forestry & Environmental Studies. https://e360.yale.edu/features/why-its-time-to-stop-punishing-our-soils-with-fertilizers-and-chemicals. Accessed January 2, 2020.

Sharma, A., P. Jha, and G. V. P. Reddy. 2018. Multidimensional relationships of herbicides with insect-crop food webs. *Science of the Total Environment* 643: 1522–1532.

Simcox, N. J., R. A. Fenske, S. A. Wolz, I. C. Lee, and D. A. Kalman. 1995. Pesticides in household dust and soil: exposure pathways for children of agricultural families. *Environmental Health Perspectives* 103(12): 1126–1134. https://doi.org/10.1289/ehp.951031126.

Silva, V., H. G. J. Mol, P. Zomer, M. Tienstra, C. J. Ritsema, and V. Geissen. 2019. Pesticide residues in European agricultural soils—A hidden reality unfolded. *Science of the Total Environment* 653: 1532–1545.

Smith, R. G., L. W. Atwood, M. B. Morris, D. A. Mortensen, and R. T. Koide. 2016. Evidence for indirect effects of pesticide seed treatments on weed seed banks in maize and soybean. *Agriculture, Ecosystems & Environment* 216: 269–273.

Stinner, B. R. and G. J. House. 1990. Arthropods and Other Invertebrates in Conservation-Tillage Agriculture. *Annual Review of Entomology*, 35(1): 299–318.

Sur, R., and A. Stork. 2003. Uptake, translocation and metabolism of imidacloprid in plants. *Bulletin of Insectology* 56: 35–40.

Thiele-Bruhn, S., J. Bloem, F. T. de Vries, K. Kalbitz, and C. Wagg. 2012. Linking soil biodiversity and agricultural soil management. *Current Opinion in Environmental Sustainability* 4: 523–528.

Tian, D., and S. Niu. 2015. A global analysis of soil acidification caused by nitrogen addition. *Environmental Research Letters* 10: 024019.

Van Hoesel, W., A. Tiefenbacher, N. König, V. M. Dorn, J. F. Hagenguth, U. Prah, T. Widhalm, V. Wiklicky, R. Koller, M. Bonkowski, J. Lagerlöf, A. Ratzenböck, and J. G. Zaller. 2017. Single and combined effects of pesticide seed dressings and herbicides on earthworms, soil microorganisms, and litter decomposition. *Frontiers in Plant Science* 8: 215.

Van Zwieten, L., J. Rust, T. Kingston, G. Merrington, and S. Morris. 2004. Influence of copper fungicide residues on occurrence of earthworms in avocado orchard soils. *Science of the Total Environment* 329: 29–41.

Wang, Shaojun, H. Chen, Y. Tan, et al. 2016. Fertilizer regime impacts on abundance and diversity of soil fauna across a poplar plantation chronosequence in coastal Eastern China. *Scientific Reports* 6: 20816.

Yardım, E. N., and C. A. Edwards. 2002. Effects of weed control practices on surface-dwelling arthropod predators in tomato agroecosystems. *Phytoparasitica* 30: 379–386.

Farming Practices that Support Soil Health

Farming practices that support soil health often need to be customized or adapted to local conditions. However, some overarching strategies are used in nearly all climate zones, soil conditions, or crop systems. Broadly speaking, some of the strategies that support soil health focus on a few key actions:

- Minimize the potential for erosion through conservation systems that protect crop fields from wind and water runoff.
- Cover the soil as much as possible year-round or maintain continuous living root systems in the soil.
- Reduce mechanical cultivation and compaction.
- Increase organic matter with natural inputs while reducing or eliminating synthetic fertilizer inputs.
- Maximize crop diversity.
- Integrate crops and livestock. For example, rotate them in succession or graze cover crops.
- Increase soil biodiversity by reducing or eliminating pesticides, including soil fumigants.

Any one of these strategies is worthy of its own book (and indeed there are lots of books on all of these topics). Moreover, most of these strategies are deeply interconnected. For example, controlling erosion, increasing soil organic matter, and maintaining living cover might all be addressed through a single practice, such as cover cropping. Describing all of the conservation practices, crop management systems, and specialized tools that can help optimize soil health seems nearly impossible. Yet, it is worth reviewing at least a few of the most established, well understood, and accessible soil conservation practices.

FIGURE 32—An example of a diverse cover crop of common vetch, spring forage pea, spring oats, triticale, purple top turnip, forage collard, safflower, sunflower, and phacelia planted in rotation with spring wheat and winter wheat in eastern Oregon.

FIGURE 33—Four Principles of Soil Health.

FIGURE 34—Terraced crop fields in Iowa.

FIGURE 35—Contour buffer strips are established around a slope, and alternate down the slope with cropped areas farmed on the contour.

FIGURE 36—Aerial view of windbreaks, rows of trees that are separating crop fields.

Erosion-Control Buffers

The loss of soil to wind and water erosion is a natural, ongoing process that occurs on most soils in both natural and agricultural settings. While this loss is typically a slow process that may be largely unnoticed in natural settings, it is often accelerated by cultivation and grazing, requiring active work to counteract erosion and keep soil on the farm. To reduce soil loss on farms, various conservation systems have been developed:

- **Terracing.** Terraces are horizontal landforms constructed on slopes to provide stable, relatively non-erodible surfaces for crop production. Examples can be found of terraced fields that have sustained continuous crop production for hundreds of years in southern Europe and Asia.

- **Contour buffer strips.** A smaller-scale version of terracing is the use of contour buffer strips where strips of perennial vegetation alternate with wider strips of row crops on sloped fields. The vegetated strips help capture sediment washing downslope in the form of sheet erosion, and they provide a barrier against rill formation.

- **Windbreaks.** Also known as shelterbelts, windbreaks consist of one or more linear row plantings of trees or shrubs surrounding farm fields, pastures, and farm buildings. In the United States, where windbreaks have been promoted since the 1930s as a soil protection feature, typical designs call for three to 10 rows of trees and shrubs. Based upon these very generalized specifications, windbreaks are typically able to reduce wind velocity for a distance of at least 20 times the windbreak height.

These conservation features help prevent the direct loss of soil from farm fields. Other conservation features, such as grassed waterways, filter strips, and riparian buffers, also exist to manage or capture eroded soil once it has been dislodged from crop fields.

No-Till Cropping

No-till and reduced-tillage cropping systems (using no-till seed drills and planters) provide good protection against soil erosion, reduce compaction, reduce disruption to fungal hyphae, and improve habitat for wildlife and beneficial insects (e.g., ground cover provided by thatch and crop residue). Additionally, no-till cropping can reduce some greenhouse gas emissions.

However, soil organic carbon (SOC) is not permanently sequestered by no-till cropping. Because no-till cropping primarily builds soil carbon in aggregates close to the soil surface, a single tillage event can lead to a large flush of microbial activity and loss of that soil organic carbon. To maintain any reduction of greenhouse gas emissions, no-till systems need to be continuously undisturbed in order to protect the soil organic carbon that is physically stabilized in soil aggregates.

Although most no-till systems are still dependent on herbicides for weed suppression, newer no-till alternatives to weed control are gaining more use, including cover crops, rotations to outcompete weeds, and roller crimpers (rather than herbicides or tillage) to terminate cover crops. Potential crop pests like slugs and voles can thrive in the crop residue of no-till fields. There are several ways to manage against these potential pests in no-till systems while supporting soil health. Create and protect perennial, bunchgrass habitat for beneficial predatory insects—including rove beetles, soldier beetles, ground beetles, and firefly larvae, which consume slugs and flatten spikes in their populations. As part of an integrated pest management plan to support populations of beneficial predatory beetles, avoid using treated seeds and insecticides. The neonicotinoids on treated cash crop seeds can kill off these beneficial insects but do not affect slugs, leaving seedlings, especially soybeans, vulnerable to slug damage. Make space on the farm landscape for coyotes and owls, which are important predators of small mammals and vital to wider agricultural and mixed land use, especially fields with cover crops and voles.

Cover Cropping

Cover crops provide temporary or permanent vegetative cover to control erosion, reduce nutrient runoff and leaching, suppress weed growth, improve soil fertility, and increase biological diversity. Farmers can customize particular cover crop mixes and management practices to meet their specific goals.

As an example, in regions with winter rainy seasons, cover crops such as triticale, cereal rye, or barley are frequently planted to reduce erosion by slowing the velocity of rainfall and preventing soil splashing. Additionally, the root systems of winter cover crops create pore spaces in the soil that enhance water infiltration, decrease surface runoff, and recharge groundwater supplies.

FIGURE 37—No-till planting of cover crops into corn residue.

FIGURE 38—A roller crimper is an implement that breaks and flattens the stems of cover crops. This is a non-chemical termination method with minimal soil disturbance.

FIGURE 39—Cover crop cocktail (crimson clover, mustard and buckwheat) in bloom.

To maximize soil fertility benefits, those who plant cover crops typically prioritize legumes that support nitrogen-fixing rhizobia, a category of bacteria. Compared to synthetic equivalents, nitrogen-fixing cover crops produce sources of fertility that are less likely to be quickly lost through denitrification or volatilization (biological conversion and loss to the atmosphere), since the nitrogen is released slowly as the cover crop decomposes. While these kinds of green manure crops have traditionally depended on tillage to be incorporated back into the soil, farmers have pioneered new roller-crimper methods to terminate cover crops and press some residue against the soil surface without tillage.

Cover crops may also consist of species that fulfill other goals, such as mustard for biofumigation to reduce soil pathogens, forage for livestock, or lacy phacelia (Phacelia tanacetifolia) to provide nectar for beneficial insects, including honey bees. Alternatively, multispecies cover crop mixes increase overall field-scale biological diversity and fill multiple ecological niches and functions. Components of multispecies cover crop mixes can range from two species to more than a dozen, including cereal grains, legumes, and oilseed crops planted in combination.

Occasionally, cover crops are also interseeded between rows of a primary cash crop. Sometimes these cover crops are planted at the same time as the primary crop. More often, they are interseeded after the primary crop is actively growing in order to reduce competition. Such systems can provide farm benefits beyond just soil health. At least one study also found that songbird densities were higher in row crops that had been intercropped with a flowering cover crop. In that study, researchers pointed to the value of the intercrop in providing cover and nesting sites for the birds, but perhaps most significant was the higher abundance of beneficial insects in the flowering intercrop.

While cover cropping is mostly used on a rotational basis with annual crops, perennial crop farmers, such as orchard and vineyard crop producers, can also maintain a continuous cover of biologically diverse vegetation. In California, Xerces biologists have worked with almond producers to test and develop flowering cover crop mixes consisting of native wildflowers for use between the rows of trees. Such perennial ground cover sometimes raises concerns about weed competition with crops, exacerbated pest or disease problems, or detrimental changes in the microclimate of the farm. However, our work and various case studies continue to show how understory plantings in perennial crop systems can successfully support beneficial insects and remain compatible with normal farm operations. Farmers should take care to minimize pesticide exposure to understory plantings designed to support beneficial insects.

Crop Rotations

Along with cover crops, nitrogen-fixing cash crops (primarily legumes, such as peas or beans) can provide an additional source of soil nitrogen. Although most research examining the benefits of crop rotations focuses on soil fertility, research also confirms that increasing crop diversity through multispecies rotations produces a corresponding increase in soil species richness. For example, one 12-year study in Michigan, led by L. K. Tiemann, compared seven different crop rotations ranging from a corn monoculture to a highly diverse rotation of multiple legumes. Researchers observed significantly higher indicators of biological activity in soils with the most diverse crop rotations, including increased decomposition rates and the presence of microbial exudates, such as glue-like compounds that form soil aggregates. Rotating annual crops with perennial forage crops, which may contain multiple species or a single species, benefits soil health by keeping the ground covered for many years, eliminating tillage and maintaining a living plant for most of the year during that portion of the rotation.

Organic Soil Inputs

When focusing on soil health, nutrient management emphasizes the role of natural inputs over synthetic ones. Common natural inputs include compost, animal manure and bedding, bone meal and blood meal, seaweed and algae, and green manure crops, especially legumes. Rotating livestock in fallowed fields provides an additional approach for manure-based fertilization. Adaptive nutrient management is important during a transition to a soil health management system and depends on cropping systems and the availability of natural inputs.

These natural inputs vary in chemical composition. They also have to decompose before the nutrients they contain are available to crops, a process that happens over an extended period of time. Nutrient release from natural inputs can also fluctuate based on temperature, soil moisture, and soil species richness. Despite the variability and slow release of natural sources of soil fertility, natural inputs eliminate some of the waste, expense, and pollution resulting from synthetic fertilizers. Care is needed in vegetable cropping systems to follow food safety rules regarding the use of animal manures.

These benefits are well illustrated in a paper by J. P. Reganold comparing wheat yields on farms in eastern Washington over an 80-year period beginning in 1908. In the earliest recorded years, all of the land was essentially farmed organically since synthetic inputs were not available. However, beginning in 1948, some of the farmland was regularly treated with synthetic fertilizers, while some of it continued to be farmed without any synthetic inputs. Researchers found that net yields were basically the same in both types of fields throughout their history. The farm not using synthetic fertilizer had less income overall because the land was fallowed every third year in a green manure crop of alfalfa. However, that farm also had lower expenses without the cost of synthetic fertilizers. The same study also revealed that the fields in a wheat and alfalfa rotation had an average of 5.9 in. (15 cm) more topsoil than the fields using synthetic fertilizers.

FIGURE 40—Turning a compost pile to aerate the compost, increase drainage and help it mature more thoroughly.

Of course, natural sources of soil fertility are dependent on complex soil food webs for decomposition. Indeed, research demonstrates greater numbers and types of soil organisms are typically found on farms managed with natural inputs. In one study, led by E. Gagnarli, comparing organic versus conventional vineyards in Italy, researchers noted that the organic soils they studied resembled undisturbed forest soils in their richness of soil life.

Ley Farming

Ley farming, in which annual crop fields are not tilled but rather are sown with a perennial cover of a grass or legume for months or years, was historically a common method of rebuilding soil health. Some farmers used fields in ley farming for hay production or livestock grazing. With the development of low-cost synthetic fertilizers in the early 20th century, ley farming was largely abandoned in favor of continuous cropping.

Despite its decline, ley farming continues to be occasionally used in rotation with crop production. In Australia, researchers have tracked the use of ley farming across more than 50 million acres, where wheat has been rotated with legume-based pasture for sheep over multiple decades. In published research findings, this system demonstrated a natural increase in soil nitrogen and water-stable aggregates, as well as 50% yield increases of wheat (when compared to continuous wheat cultivation). Similarly, case studies from Argentina have demonstrated the successful elimination of synthetic fertilizers from grain fields where rotational ley farming is practiced. Despite the fact that rotational ley farming has been used for centuries, contemporary research on the practice remains limited, especially research related to ley farming and soil biodiversity. However, one study

FIGURE 41—One way that an Indiana farm integrates livestock into annual crop rotations is to graze cattle on the cover crop (wheat) prior to termination.

of rotational ley farming, led by K. Y. Chan, found the highest numbers of earthworms occurring during the second year of grass-legume ley farming, while the populations dropped to their lowest levels during active cash crop production.

Support for Soil Health Practices

The NRCS and the USDA Farm Service Agency (FSA) provide technical and financial assistance to support conservation efforts for soil health and wildlife on working agricultural lands. Agricultural producers can use conservation programs such as the Environmental Quality Incentives Program (EQIP), Conservation Stewardship Program (CSP), and Conservation Reserve Program (CRP) to help establish soil health practices that support soil organisms, such as cover cropping or planting permanent ground cover. The NRCS also provides free technical assistance to landowners and managers through the Conservation Technical Assistance (CTA) program, and can help develop conservation plans to address resource or habitat concerns. Table 1 includes conservation practices available through the NRCS that can support soil organisms and other conservation goals. For information on conservation programs or technical assistance, contact your local NRCS, FSA, or conservation district office. The office nearest you can be located at **http://offices.sc.egov.usda.gov/locator/app**.

FIGURE 42—NRCS staff provide technical assistance to producers, including creating custom plans to conserve soil and address other resource concerns.

References

Cederbaum, S. B., J. P. Carroll, and R. J. Cooper. 2004. Effects of alternative cotton agriculture on avian and arthropod populations. *Conservation Biology* 18: 1272–1282.

Chan, K. Y. 2001. An overview of some tillage impacts on earthworm population abundance and diversity—implications for functioning in soils. *Soil and Tillage Research* 57 (4): 179–191.

Chaney, R. L. 2012. Food safety issues for mineral and organic fertilizers. *Advances in Agronomy* 117: 51–99.

Gagnarli, E., D. Goggioli, F. Tarchi, S. Guidi, R. Nannelli, N. Vignozzi, G. Valboa, M. R. Lottero, L. Corino, and S. Simini. 2015. Case study of microarthropod communities to assess soil quality in different managed vineyards. *SOIL* 1: 527–536.

Giller, K. E., and G. Cadisch. 1995. Future benefits from biological nitrogen fixation: An ecological approach to agriculture. *Plant and Soil* 174: 255–277.

Joyce, B. A., W. W. Wallender, J. P. Mitchell, L. M. Huyck, S. R. Temple, P. N. Brostrom, T. C. Hsiao. 2002. Infiltration and soil water storage under winter cover cropping in California's Sacramento Valley. *Transactions of the ASAE* 45: 315–326.

Reeves, T.G. 1987. Temperate pastures: Their production, use, and management. In *Pastures in cropping systems*. Australian Wool Cooperation/CSRIO, Sydney. 501–515.

Reganold, J. P., L. F. Elliott, and Y. L. Unger. 1987. Long-term effects of organic and conventional farming on soil erosion. *Nature* 330, 6146: 370–372.

Reganold, J.P. 1988. Comparison of soil properties as influenced by organic and conventional farming systems. *American Journal of Alternative Agriculture* 3,4: 144–155.

Tiemann, L. K., A. S. Grandy, E. E. Atkinson, E. Marin-Spiotta, and M. D. McDaniel. 2015. Crop rotational diversity enhances belowground communities and functions in an agroecosystem. *Ecology Letters* 18(8): 761–771. https://doi.org/10.1111/ele.12453.

Warburton D., and W. Klimstra. 1984. Wildlife use of no-till and conventionally tilled corn fields. *Journal of Soil and Water Conservation*. 39: 327–330.

The Life in Soil

As the title *Farming for Soil Life* indicates, soil is a living system. It is both the product and producer of dynamic interactions between life above the soil surface and below it. Most plants cannot grow without soil, and healthy soil cannot form without the contribution of plants and microbes. Once the process of soil formation is started and maintained, healthy soils are full of life.

Organisms that live in the soil are diverse and numerous. This section focuses on the function, ecology, and identification of animals in the soil and how to observe and promote this life. We begin the discussion of organisms with light coverage of microflora, fungi, and plants. Then, under Soil Fauna, the animal profiles are organized by body size: microfauna, mesofauna, and macrofauna (see figure 1), then by biological classification. Large groups (e.g., beetles and flies) are further clustered by ecology.

Microflora

Bacteria are ubiquitous, microbial organisms often growing and living in colonies of individuals. The total biomass of living bacteria is estimated to exceed the biomass of all plants and animals on Earth combined. As a group, bacteria play an important role in organic matter decomposition. Relevant to soil life, the groups Rhizobium, Azotobacter, and Frankia form associations with plant roots and are essential in nitrogen fixation and the nitrogen cycle. *Cyanobacteria* form nitrogen-fixing associations with certain plant groups, including gymnosperms (e.g., conifers and cycads) and ferns, some lichens, algae, and mosses. Species of Agrobacterium may be pathogenic in some soil conditions.

Archaea are single-celled microorganisms that are present in terrestrial and marine environments and within other organisms, and some archaea are adapted to extreme conditions (e.g., hot springs and saline environments). These microorganisms have the ability to use hydrogen and other ions for energy in addition to organic (carbon-based) energy sources. Archaea contribute to nutrient cycling (especially in the nitrogen cycle), and ecologically they are either beneficial (mutualists) or neutral (commensalists). No pathogenic Archaea have been described.

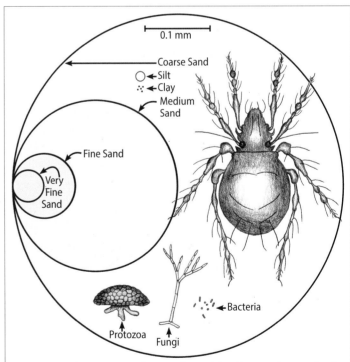

FIGURE 43—Relative sizes of six soil particle classes, three microbe groups, and a soil mite. (Adapted from J. Nardi 2007, Chicago University Press.)

Fungi

Fungi are extremely diverse in shape, size, form, and function. Some are unicellular and are present as individuals or colonies in the soil. Others are multicellular. Most fungi are beneficial to plants. They cycle nutrients and provide mechanisms for plant nutrient acquisition and water uptake. Arbuscular mycorrhizal (endomycorrhizal) fungi (AMF) interact with host plant cells and make special connections in the roots of plants that enhance nutrient and water uptake. They do not form fruiting bodies; instead, spores form directly from the hyphae. More than 80% of plant species on land have associations with arbuscular mycorrhizal fungi. Ectomycorrhizal fungi inhabit the spaces between cells in plant roots and expand the plant's ability to uptake water and nutrients from the soil. Ectomycorrhizal fungi produce distinctive fruiting bodies for sexual reproduction.

The fungi we call mushrooms are mostly basidiomycetes and ascomycetes. Mushrooms are like icebergs in that what we can't see underneath the surface is much larger than the part that we can observe. These groups of fungi are present in the soil as extensive and complex networks of threadlike hyphae collectively called mycelia. The networks transport energy, minerals, and chemical signals; grow by cell division; and reproduce sexually by spore production in special fruiting bodies called mushrooms. Some fungi are pathogens, but overall, fungi are beneficial, either as

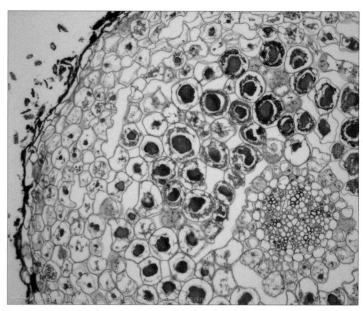

Figure 44—The red-stained structures of arbuscular mycorrhizal fungi (AMF) within the root cells of a vascular plant. The symbiotic relationship between plant roots and AMF occurs in 80% of plant species and is a mechanism for the exchange of phosphorus, carbon, water, and other nutrients between plants, soil and the fungi.

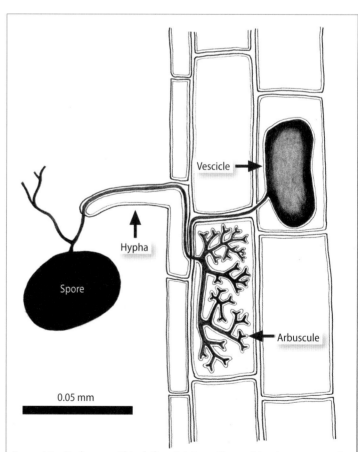

Figure 46—Endomycorrhizal fungi interacting with plant root cells. (Adapted from J. Nardi 2007, Chicago University Press.)

Figure 45—Close-up of mycelium—the vegetative part of fungus comprised of branches of hyphae— in the soil.

saprophytes that decompose plants and animals and make those nutrients available for renewed uptake, or through symbiotic relationships with plant roots. A few species are even predatory, trapping nematodes.

Plants

Soil and plants are intrinsically linked. An individual plant is simultaneously an aboveground and belowground organism. Vascular land plants need soil as a substrate for anchoring and as their source of water and nutrients. Conversely, plants contribute to soil formation by breaking down mineral substrates. In the early stages of soil formation, lichens, moss, and cryptobiotic crusts and the roots of plants break down bedrock. Some plant root systems can act as a net that holds mineral soil and organic matter, further adding to soil formation. In mature soils, plants are crucial to soil health and soil life. Plants feed soil life by secreting carbohydrates produced through photosynthesis into the root zone, called the rhizosphere. These carbohydrates, referred to as exudates, are released both actively and passively. The exudation from roots is not just accidental, but the basis of an environment for a mutually beneficial and symbiotic relationship between plants and soil microbes. Seeds in the soil are food for birds, invertebrates, and microbes.

Soil Fauna

The role of microbes in soil ecology and function has long been acknowledged; in contrast, the role of soil fauna, though significant, has been overlooked. Soil fauna can alter the physical structure of soil; facilitate the movement of air, water, and roots within the soil; and help circulate nutrients between soil layers. Soil mesofauna and macrofauna are instrumental in nutrient cycling, helping to fragment plant and animal organic matter and making it more available to further decomposition by microbes. Food-web relationships of soil fauna are complex and include herbivores that feed on dead plant material or directly on roots of living plants or algae, as well as communities of predators and parasites that feed on soil fauna. Despite their importance to soil systems, there are knowledge gaps in the natural history and biology of many identified species, and many others remain undescribed and unnamed. There is still much to learn about soil life!

Figure 47—A diversity of plant forms from many families such as the trees, perennial wildflowers, grasses and berry crops shown here support more diverse underground communities of microbes and invertebrates than monocultures or areas with low plant diversity.

Soil Fauna, Classified by General Body Length

FAUNA	GROUP	SIZE RANGE (METRIC / INCHES)
Micro	Protozoa	1 µm–3mm / 0.00004–0.11"
Meso	Rotifers	0.1–3 mm / 0.0039–0.12"
	Tardigrades	0.05–1.7 mm / 0.002–0.067"
	Nematodes	0.3–10 mm / 0.012–0.39"
	Potworms	1–30 mm / 0.039–1.18"
	Mites	60 µm–5 mm / 0.0024–0.2"
	Springtails	0.25–5 mm / 0.0098–0.2"
	Bristletails	2–15 mm / 0.079–0.59"
	Thrips	0.5–5 mm / 0.02–0.2"
	Dwarf millipedes	1–10 mm / 0.039–0.39"
Macro	Earthworms	1–40 mm / 0.39–15.7"
	Slugs, snails	1.5 mm–12 cm / 0.059–4.7"
	Spiders	1–35 mm / 0.079–1.18"
	Termites	2–20 mm / 0.08–0.8"
	Flies	1 mm–3.5 cm / 0.039–1.38"
	Beetles	0.5 mm–12 cm / 0.02–4.72"
	Ants	1–25 mm / 0.04–0.98"
	Bees, wasps	1 mm–5 cm / 0.039–1.18"

Notes About the Profiles

Here we provide profiles of fauna that live in the soil throughout their life and species that spend most of their lives in the soil, emerging for short portions of their life cycle. We also include fauna that are more transient, spending only a small portion of their life in the soil, or that live in decaying plant, fungi, or animal matter that will eventually return to the soil. Each profile focuses on the most common and studied members of the group. However, for many soil invertebrates that have not yet been researched in detail, complete information on the number of species or relative abundance or life cycle is currently unavailable.

Soil Fauna Profiles:

SOIL MICROFAUNA are tiny creatures, less than 0.006" (0.16 mm). Microfauna inhabit water films and studying them often requires microbiological techniques, including preparing and looking at specimens under magnification.

MICROFAUNA ▷ ▷ ▷ ▷ ▷

1. PROTOZOANS

KINGDOM: Protozoa* ▷ **PHYLA:** Amoebozoa, Cercozoa, Ciliophora

  The classification of different protozoan groups is in constant fluctuation as scientists better understand how these organisms are related to each other and to other groups. Currently the groups included in the kingdom Protozoa may not all share a common ancestor. Some protozoans are more closely related to (but do not belong in) the animal kingdom, while others are more closely related to the plant or fungus kingdom.

SIZE: 0.00004–0.11" (1 μm–3 mm).

ECOLOGICAL ROLE: As predators, decomposers, and consumers of bacteria, protozoans play a significant role in nutrient cycling.

DESCRIPTION: These single-celled organisms are diverse in shape and size. Some are colonial and live in clusters, resembling multicellular organisms. Amoebae (Amoebozoa) have pseudopods—temporary projections filled with cytoplasm that they can extend and retract to move into soil crevices and alter their shape. Testate amoebae (Amoebozoa) have a shell-like test made of organic, siliceous, or calcareous materials

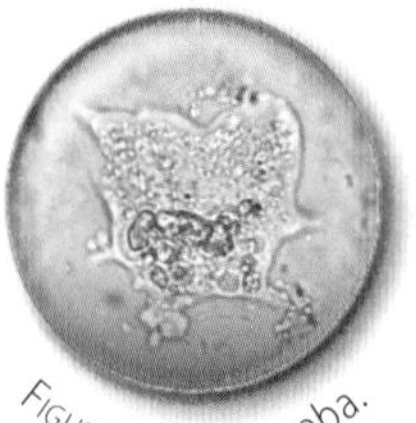

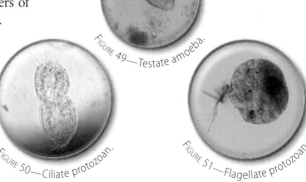

FIGURE 48—Amoeba.

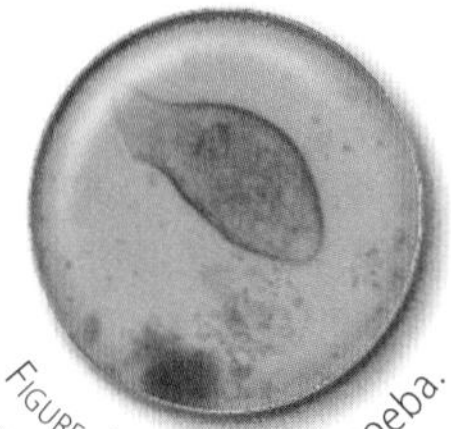

FIGURE 49—Testate amoeba.

FIGURE 50—Ciliate protozoan.

FIGURE 51—Flagellate protozoan.

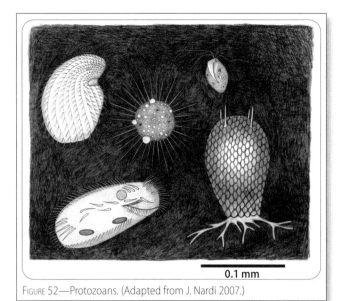

FIGURE 52—Protozoans. (Adapted from J. Nardi 2007.)

0.1 mm

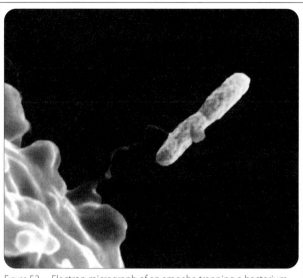

FIGURE 53—Electron micrograph of an amoeba trapping a bacterium.

depending on the species that partially encloses the cell. Ciliate protozoans (Ciliophora) have cilia, structures that help them move or sense their environment. Flagellate protozoans (Cercozoa) have one or more whiplike organs that propel them.

WHERE THEY ARE FOUND: Protozoans are found within water films in and on soil and other moist surfaces. Although they are most common in the upper few centimeters of soil among plant roots, some can be found at depths of more than 219 yd. (200 m). Amoebae in particular are able to fit into very small pores or soil cavities.

WHAT THEY EAT: Protozoans primarily feed on bacteria, though larger protozoans can also feed on algae, fungus, or small organic debris, releasing nutrients that stimulate plant growth.

LIFE CYCLE: Protozoans can reproduce asexually by duplicating their body and splitting themselves into two organisms, but many species can also exchange genetic material through conjugation. When soils dry out, protozoans become cysts—inactive states in which they are in suspended animation until more moisture arrives.

APPROX. NUMBER OF KNOWN SPECIES: 3,000 Amoebozoa, 100–1,000+ Cercozoa (many undescribed), and 1,500 Ciliophora worldwide.

RELATIVE ABUNDANCE: Some estimates suggest that 10 billion protozoans can live in the top 6" (15.24 cm) of a square yard of meadow. Protozoans with flagella are the most common overall. Amoebae without shells (pseudopods) are more common in wet soils, while testate amoebae are more common in forest soil than in plowed fields.

NOTES OF INTEREST:

- Protozoans are the primary consumers of bacteria in soil.
- Protozoans are sensitive to environmental changes, and changes in their distribution and activity relate to changes in soil health.
- Some groups of organisms were once thought to be fungi or plants and are now considered protists (at least for the time being). These include brown algae found in the soil and slime and water molds.
- Brown algae in the soil have lost the ability to photosynthesize; instead, they absorb nutrients by extending filaments into decomposing tissues or living plant material.
- The oomycete protist *Phytophthora infestans* was the pathogen that contributed to the Irish potato famine in the 1840s.
- One method for counting protozoans: use a microscope to count protozoans directly from soil samples in a suspension in small wells or in a petri dish.

MESOFAUNA)) NON-ARTHROPODS

2. ROTIFERS

PHYLUM: Rotifera » **CLASS:** Bdelloidea

SIZE: 0.0039–0.12" (0.1–3 mm).

ECOLOGICAL ROLE: Rotifers are predators and scavengers.

DESCRIPTION: Since rotifers are so small, only a few features are recognizable under a microscope. These features include crowns of cilia on their heads that whirl in circular patterns and are used in swimming and in filter feeding, a set of hard jaws, and a foot that is occasionally used to scoot across surfaces.

WHERE THEY ARE FOUND: Rotifers are aquatic organisms, but many live in the soil in water films, mostly near the surface. They are also found on mosses or lichens and in leaf litter in forests.

WHAT THEY EAT: Rotifers consume bacteria, protozoa, fungi, and algae. They are vortex feeders, using their cilia to create a current to draw in food.

LIFE CYCLE: When water films disappear in the soil, rotifers form cysts, a stage of resting animation while they wait for moisture. This stage allows them to survive dry conditions; they can be transported to other habitats during this stage. Soil rotifers reproduce without sex; males are absent entirely and females reproduce via unfertilized eggs.

APPROX. NUMBER OF KNOWN SPECIES: 2,030 worldwide, with only about 5% found in soil.

RELATIVE ABUNDANCE: They may exceed 100,000 per square meter in moist soils.

NOTES OF INTEREST:

- Their name is derived from the Latin for wheel bearer.
- Their vortex feeding can be readily observed under a microscope.
- Some form shells that incorporate body secretions, debris, or fecal material.
- Rotifers can be extracted from soil samples using methods similar to those used for nematodes.

FIGURE 54—Rotifer colony.

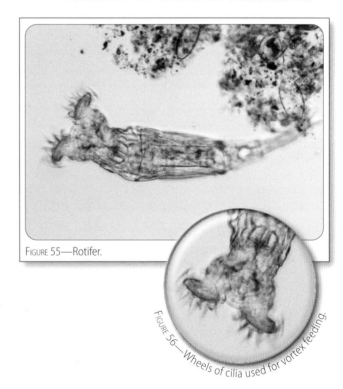

FIGURE 55—Rotifer.

FIGURE 56—Wheels of cilia used for vortex feeding.

ROTIFERS

3. TARDIGRADES

PHYLUM: Tardigrada » **CLASSES:** Eutardigrada, Heterotardigrada
SIZE: 0.002–0.067" (0.05–1.7 mm).
ECOLOGICAL ROLE: Tardigrades are predators and omnivores in soil food webs.
DESCRIPTION: Earning their nickname "little water bears," tardigrades have bodies with the appearance of segmentation and eight stubby legs that end in several short claws. They can be brown, white, green, orange, pink, or even colorless altogether. They have mouthparts used to pierce food sources and suck out fluids.
WHERE THEY ARE FOUND: Tardigrades are predominantly found in the top 1" (2.54 cm) of soil, though some are also found in deeper layers. They can live in leaf litter and water—both marine and freshwater—and they occur in just about every habitat from the poles to the equator, including deep seas and mountains.
WHAT THEY EAT: Some are carnivorous, feeding on protozoa, nematodes, and rotifers; others consume plants, algae, or fungi.
LIFE CYCLE: Tardigrade eggs can be ornate, with geometric patterns and spines, ridges, and more. In suspended animation, adult tardigrades become shriveled up after losing nearly all the water in their body, a state that closely resembles death. With their metabolism slowed to 0.01% of their normal rate, they only reanimate when in contact with water.
APPROX. NUMBER OF KNOWN SPECIES: 1,500 worldwide.
RELATIVE ABUNDANCE: Tardigrades can be very abundant under certain conditions (when there's enough moisture, food, and proper temperatures), with up to approximately 400,000 per square yard.

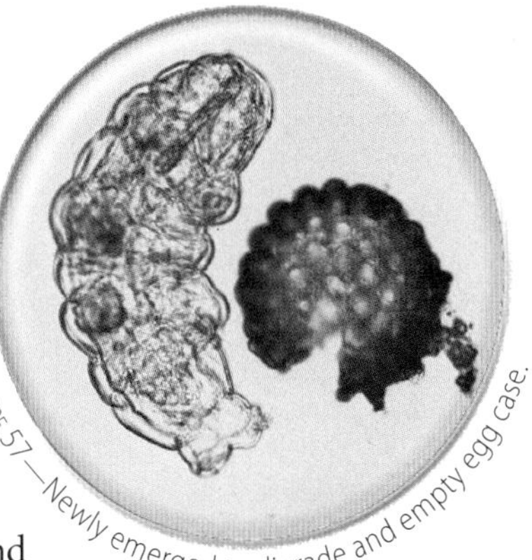

FIGURE 57—Newly emerged tardigrade and empty egg case.

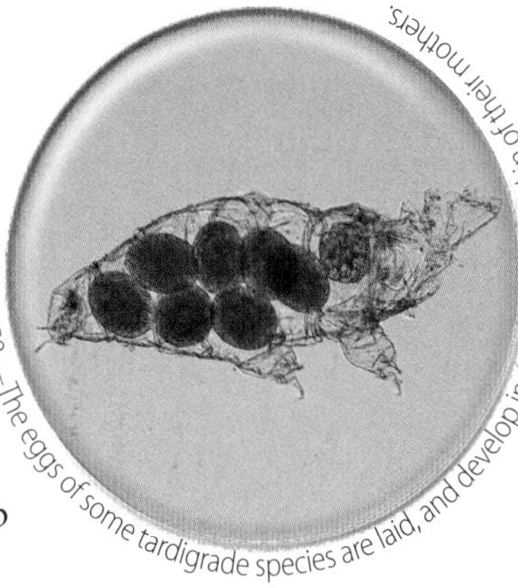

FIGURE 58—The eggs of some tardigrade species are laid, and develop inside, the cast-off skin of their mothers.

TARDIGRADES

NOTES OF INTEREST:

- The term cryptobiosis is derived from Greek for hidden (*crypto*) and life (*bios*), an apt name to describe the state of an organism when it shows no visible signs of life.

- They may be indicators of environmental stress. Certain species can flourish in certain environments, and tardigrade species richness and abundance can indicate levels of pollution.

- Some tardigrades can be very long-lived. Researchers have reanimated individuals after 30 years of being frozen. (In the 1940s, a researcher claimed to reanimate a tardigrade after 120 years on a moss specimen in a museum, but this hasn't been replicated).

- Tardigrades were only described about 200 years ago. We still have a lot to learn and there are many undescribed species.

- One reason for interest in tardigrades is to determine if cryptobiosis is a possibility for humans as well.

- Tardigrades can recover after immersion in liquid nitrogen.

- Other common names include moss piglets and slow walkers.

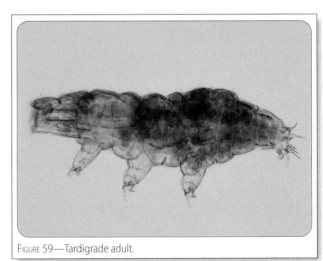

FIGURE 59—Tardigrade adult.

- Tardigrades are resistant to cosmic radiation and vacuums—nearly 70% of tardigrades sent into orbit in 2007 survived the 10-day trip and return to Earth. An Israeli spacecraft carrying thousands of tardigrades in their cryptobiotic state crash-landed on the moon in 2019.

4. NEMATODES (EELWORMS)

PHYLUM: Nematoda » **CLASSES:** Chromadorea, Enoplea » **ORDERS:** Aphelenchida, Dorylaimida, Mononchida, Rhabditida, Tylenchida

SIZE: 0.012–0.39" (0.3–10 mm).

ECOLOGICAL ROLE: Nematodes have several roles in soil life based on the foods they eat. They are variously predators, omnivores, fungivores, bacterivores, and plant parasites. Additionally, as nematodes move through the soil, they carry and excrete bacteria, helping bacteria to disperse throughout soil layers.

DESCRIPTION: Nematodes are unsegmented, slender worms with an elongated cylindrical body that tapers at both ends. Their bodies are usually somewhat transparent. Their mouthparts are specialized for their eating habits: Those that are predatory have teeth lining their mouth. Root and fungi feeders have needlelike, piercing mouthparts to puncture plants or fungi and withdraw fluids. Bacteria feeders have "lips."

WHERE THEY ARE FOUND: Nematodes are found in all types of soils and habitats, including aquatic environments and even polar regions. However, only a small percentage of species have wide distributions; most are endemic to a region or site. They primarily inhabit water films or water-filled pores in soils.

WHAT THEY EAT: Different groups of nematodes eat different trophic groups: there are bacteria feeders, fungal feeders, plant feeders (feeding on roots or algae), and predators that consume protozoa, rotifers, tardigrades, other nematodes, and tiny soil insects.

LIFE CYCLE: Nematodes depend on water films in soil for air-gas exchange. They can survive in harsh conditions, including drought or extreme cold or heat, by entering a dormant state. Many species have males and females, but some are hermaphroditic or parthenogenetic (producing only females through asexual reproduction). Nematodes develop from eggs through four juvenile stages before reaching the adult stage. Some species have quick reproduction while others are longer lived with lower reproduction rates.

APPROX. NUMBER OF KNOWN SPECIES: 25,000 worldwide. Many more remain undescribed.

RELATIVE ABUNDANCE: Nematodes are among the most numerous animals on the planet. Estimates include more than a million individuals per square meter. They are most abundant in grasslands and pasture soils, with estimates of up to 80 billion per acre; cultivated fields support about eight billion individuals per acre. Predatory and fungal-feeding nematodes are less abundant in disturbed soils.

NOTES OF INTEREST:

- Nematodes are also called eelworms and occasionally referred to as roundworms, though the latter can also refer to a specific group of nematodes that are internal parasites of humans, pets, livestock, and other animals.
- Nematodes can be indicators of environmental quality. Species that reproduce quickly following the addition of nutrients are considered colonizers, while longer-lived species with low reproduction rates are deemed persisters.
- Some have been found feeding on bacteria in soil as deep as 2.2 mi. (3.5 km), deeper than any animal.
- Plant-parasitic nematodes can cause serious economic damage to crops, especially corn, soybean, rice, and citrus.
- Some soil fungi trap and consume nematodes.

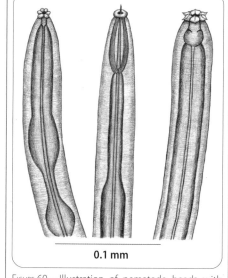

FIGURE 60—Illustration of nematode heads with mouthparts specialized for feeding. The nematode on the left feeds on bacteria, the middle nematode feeds on plant roots or fungi, and the nematode on the right has teeth used to feed on other nematodes or rotifers. (J. Nardi 2007).

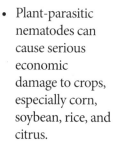

FIGURE 61—Microscopic nematode.

FIGURE 62—Overwintering grasshopper nematode (Mermis nigrescens).

- Some nematodes are intestinal parasites in humans and are the source of human health issues (e.g., hookworm, Guinea worm, and filarial worm that causes elephantiasis). A number of species parasitize other vertebrates, and some also parasitize invertebrates.
- Dr. N. A. Cobb wrote in the *1914 Yearbook of the United States Department of Agriculture*, "If all matter in the universe except the nematodes were swept away, our world would still be dimly recognizable… We should find its mountains, hills, vales, rivers, lakes, and oceans represented by a film of nematodes…We must therefore conceive of nematodes and their eggs as almost omnipresent."
- Nematodes may seek out "hot spots" of organic matter in the soil, such as in the rhizosphere.

- Nematodes are very resilient; species taken onboard for study survived the 2003 NASA space shuttle Columbia crash.
- Some nematodes can survive long-term exposure to cold, dry conditions. In 1945, scientists revived five individuals of the species *Tylenchus polyhypnus* from a rye leaf of a 39-year-old herbarium specimen. *Plectus murrayi* nematodes were revived from Antarctic moss specimens after 25 years of storage. Samples of Pleistocene permafrost from 32,000–42,000-year-old glacial deposits contained viable soil nematodes (*Panagrolaimus* spp. and *Plectus* spp.), indicating that such organisms can survive tens of thousands of years of cryptobiosis.
- Baermann funnels can be used to extract nematodes from soil samples.

5. POTWORMS

PHYLUM: Annelida » CLASS: Clitellata » ORDER: Haplotaxida » FAMILY: Enchytraeidae

SIZE: 0.039–1.18" (1–30 mm).

ECOLOGICAL ROLE: Potworms influence soil primarily through their feeding and increase the integration of organic matter and minerals. Potworms may also increase soil porosity, proportionate to their body size. In addition to their role as ecosystem engineers, potworms are important decomposers and consumers of plant material, fungi, and bacteria.

DESCRIPTION: Potworms are similar in shape to earthworms, though smaller overall. They are unpigmented, and each segment has a bundle of bristles used to anchor to surfaces.

WHERE THEY ARE FOUND: Potworms occur primarily in soils that have lots of decaying matter and are most common in the upper soil layer, about 0.39" (5 cm) deep. These worms also seem to prefer acid soils.

WHAT THEY EAT: Potworms consume fungi, bacteria, decaying organic material such as litter or roots, and fecal matter of soil macrofauna. Potworms also ingest minerals and soil particles.

LIFE CYCLE: Individuals are hermaphroditic, possessing both female and male reproductive organs. Potworms can reproduce by mutually exchanging sperm and eggs, through parthenogenesis, or by completely regenerating from pieces broken from their body. Potworms lay eggs in cocoons that are formed by secretions, and newly hatched individuals mature after 65 to 120 days.

APPROX. NUMBER OF KNOWN SPECIES: 700 worldwide (177 in North America). Many more species remain undescribed.

RELATIVE ABUNDANCE: One estimate puts about 400 million potworms in an acre of grassland soil. In heavily cultivated soil, densities are lower (less than 1,000 individuals per square meter) compared with uncultivated soils (140,000 individuals per square meter in a peat bog in the United Kingdom).

NOTES OF INTEREST:
- Ice worms (*Mesenchytraeus* spp.) live in glaciers and cannot survive at temperatures much above freezing.
- Their common name apparently is derived from their first discovery in flowerpots.
- They can be sampled using a soil core and a Baermann funnel.

FIGURE 63—Potworms.

ARTHROPOD SOIL MESOFAUNA (a.k.a. "mesoarthropods") are small arthropods that impact decomposition processes. They are important links in food webs—feeding on fungi, nematodes, and more—and are food sources themselves for larger arthropods like beetles and ants. Mesoarthropods can be abundant in their habitats. This group indirectly influences soil structure by contributing their bodies to the organic matter of soil. Mesoarthropods are too small and numerous to count in the field, and samples are brought back to a lab in order to extract and identify mesoarthropods. Berlese funnels are often used to extract mesoarthropods from the soil, or they can be extracted by floating a sample in solvents, followed by filtering.

6. MITES

PHYLUM: Arthropoda » **CLASS:** Arachnida » **SUBCLASS:** Acari » **ORDERS:** Mesostigmata, Oribatida

SIZE: 0.0024–0.2" (60 µm–5 mm).

ECOLOGICAL ROLE: Mites are critical in soil food webs as decomposers and predators. Particularly important in their role as detritivores, oribatid mites break down leaf litter into pieces accessible to smaller decomposers. Mites are also agents of bacterial and fungal dispersal.

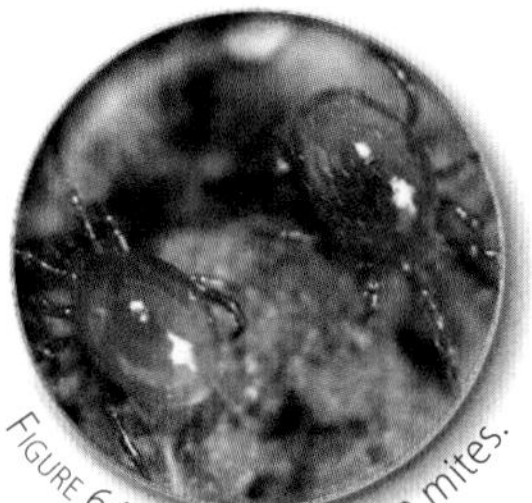

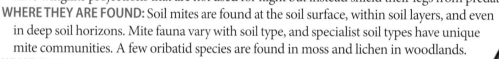

FIGURE 64—Mesostigmata mites.

DESCRIPTION: Mites have rounded or pear-shaped bodies with a cuticle that ranges from soft or very hard but that is typically dark in coloration. Adult mites have eight legs and larvae have six. Some species have simple eyes, while others are blind and rely on hairlike setae for sensing. One group of oribatid mites have hard shells with a hinge that opens the shell, allowing them to tuck their legs inside the shell for protection, resembling a small seed. Others have winglike projections that are not used for flight but instead shield their legs from predators.

WHERE THEY ARE FOUND: Soil mites are found at the soil surface, within soil layers, and even in deep soil horizons. Mite fauna vary with soil type, and specialist soil types have unique mite communities. A few oribatid species are found in moss and lichen in woodlands.

FIGURE 65—Oribatid mite.

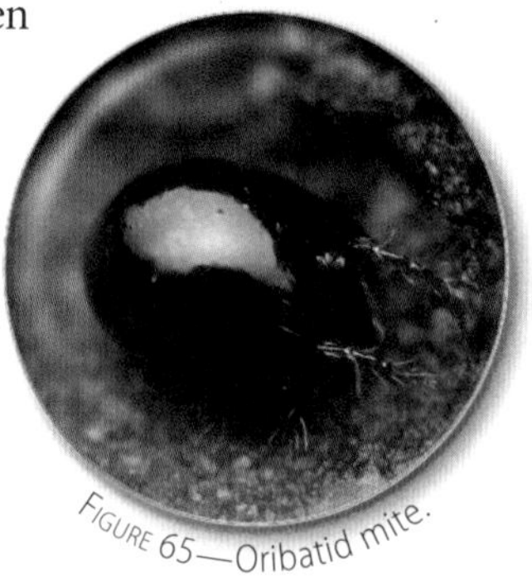

WHAT THEY EAT: Oribatid mites consume bacteria, fungi, algae, and dead plants and animals, while mites of the order Mesostigmata eat soil animals such as insect eggs and larvae, other mites, springtails, and nematodes.

LIFE CYCLE: Mites pass through egg, prelarva, larva, and several nymphal stages before becoming adults. The length of each life cycle varies significantly by species, from weeks to up to three years. Some species can reproduce by parthenogenesis, in which diploid eggs develop into female mites without fertilization.

APPROX. NUMBER OF KNOWN SPECIES: 28,000 worldwide (1,850 in North America).

RELATIVE ABUNDANCE: Among soil arthropods, mites have the most species and often the highest abundance in most types of soil. For example, about 250,000 mites can live in a square meter of moist forest soil. A 100-gram sample of soil may include as many as 500 individuals representing about 100 genera.

NOTES OF INTEREST:

- Nearly 40% of all microarthropods in the soil are mites.
- Fungi and oribatid mites seem to compete for decaying plant litter (either is dominant at a site but not both).
- An oribatid mite eats about 20% of its weight in leaf litter every day. They are essential for creating further breakdown of materials by other decomposers, and they stimulate microbial activity by dispersing bacteria and fungi. Their share in turning over soil substances is estimated to be 50%.
- Some mites can disperse to new habitats by hitching a ride on insects (e.g., clinging to the hairs of ground-nesting bees during flight, then dropping in a new location).
- Mites in the small family Nematalycidae reside in deep soil and have a more wormlike body shape.
- Non-soil-dwelling mites can be found everywhere, in all types of aquatic habitat (even hot springs and deep trenches) and terrestrial habitats, too.
- The composition of mite communities can be indicators of past vegetation and landscapes.
- Many species need to be mounted on slides in order to be identified.
- Tillage can reduce predatory mite populations in crops.
- Mites are pretty resistant to radioactivity. They can withstand doses 100× more than a lethal dose to humans.

7. DWARF MILLIPEDES (SYMPHYLANS)

PHYLUM: Arthropoda » **SUBPHYLUM:** Myriapoda » **CLASS:** Symphyla
SIZE: 0.039–0.39" (1–10 mm).
ECOLOGICAL ROLE: In food webs, dwarf millipedes are decomposers, herbivores, fungivores, and scavengers.
DESCRIPTION: Dwarf millipedes are white or colorless, with elongated, segmented bodies and 12 pairs of legs. They are usually eyeless but have long, beaded antennae. On their last abdominal segment, dwarf millipedes have spinnerets used to spin silk to deter predators.
WHERE THEY ARE FOUND: Dwarf millipedes are found in deep and shallow layers of the soil, often among roots. They move through pore spaces in the soil.
WHAT THEY EAT: These myriapods feed on decaying vegetation, fungi, and dead animals, and some are root feeders.
LIFE CYCLE: Young are born with six pairs of legs and add legs as they molt. There are one or two generations per year.
APPROX. NUMBER OF KNOWN SPECIES: 200 worldwide (30 in North America).
RELATIVE ABUNDANCE: These arthropods can be locally abundant.
NOTES OF INTEREST:

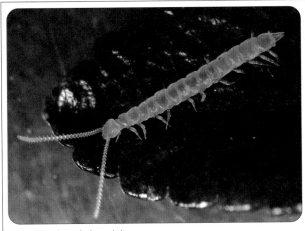

FIGURE 66—Symphylan adult.

- Dwarf millipedes may vertically migrate in the soil, moving with moisture as it changes through the seasons, becoming more abundant in upper layers in autumn and spring, then moving deeper in dryer summer periods.
- One root-feeding species, the garden symphlylan (Scutigerella immaculata), can cause damage to crops.

8. PAUROPODS

PHYLUM: Arthropoda » **SUBPHYLUM:** Myriapoda » **CLASS:** Pauropoda
SIZE: 0.02–0.08" (0.5–2 mm).
ECOLOGICAL ROLE: In food webs, pauropods are decomposers, and their ecological roles are not well understood.
DESCRIPTION: Pauropods are pale, with 11 to 12 body segments and nine to 10 pairs of legs. They are usually eyeless and have forked or branched antennae.
WHERE THEY ARE FOUND: Pauropods are found in soil, decaying wood, leaf litter, and other moist, dark places.
WHAT THEY EAT: These myriapods feed on decaying organic matter and fungi.
LIFE CYCLE: Pauropods have separate sexes, though parthenogenesis may occur in some species. Young resemble adults and add segments and legs as they molt.
APPROX. NUMBER OF KNOWN SPECIES: 500 worldwide (100 in North America).
RELATIVE ABUNDANCE: Pauropods are not abundant (usually less than 100 per square meter).
NOTES OF INTEREST:

- This group is not well studied, and many species remain undescribed. In a 2002 study, more than 30 species were found in the Great Smoky Mountains National Park that had not yet been described, eight of which were new to science.
- The best way to sample these arthropods is with a Berlese funnel.

FIGURE 67—Pauropod.

9. SPRINGTAILS

PHYLUM: Arthropoda » **CLASS:** Collembola » **ORDERS:** Entomobryomorpha, Neelipleona, Poduromorpha, Symphypleona » **FAMILIES:** Entomobryidae, Hypogastruridae, Onychiuridae, Sminthuridae

SIZE: 0.0098–0.2" (0.25–5 mm).

ECOLOGICAL ROLE: As decomposers, springtails impact nitrogen mineralization and plant growth. Their selective consumption of fungi can also alter fungal communities and may contribute indirectly to nutrient cycling and the decomposition process.

DESCRIPTION: Springtails range in body shape from elongate to globular and compact and from white to purple to brown or gray in body color. Many have a structure that looks like a tail and extends from the back of the body; this structure, called a furcula, is held under tension beneath the abdomen until released, when it will propel the springtail on the soil surface in a short jump more than 20 times its own body length (hence their common name). Species that dwell within the soil have a reduced or absent furcula. Simple eyes are present in some species, but species that dwell deep in the soil are blind.

FIGURE 68—Entomobryid springtail (Pogonognathellus sp.).

FIGURE 69—Sminthurid springtail.

WHERE THEY ARE FOUND: Entomobryomorpha and Symphypleona springtails live in soil surface litter and vegetation, decaying logs, and fungi, as well as under bark. Poduromorpha and Neelipleona dwell within the soil. Springtails occur in all terrestrial habitats, from deserts to rainforests to mountains to seashores, and are dominant in Arctic soils.

WHAT THEY EAT: Springtails consume decaying plants, fungi, bacteria, and pollen. Some are predators of rotifers, nematodes, and other springtails. A few species may consume plant roots, occasionally becoming economically damaging.

LIFE CYCLE: Springtails have simple metamorphosis but unlike insects, they continue to molt after becoming mature, with some molting up to 50 times in their life. (Arthropods must shed their skin, or molt, in order to grow. An instar is a developmental stage in between molts. Maturity in springtails is usually at the fifth or sixth instar.) Most are bisexual, and some species have parthenogenetic forms.

APPROX. NUMBER OF KNOWN SPECIES: 8,500 worldwide (840 in North America).

RELATIVE ABUNDANCE: Springtails can be quite abundant. Populations of 1.4 billion per acre have been estimated in some places; in temperate grasslands, up to 40,000 per square foot have been recorded.

NOTES OF INTEREST:

- Tillage can reduce populations of springtails.
- Blind springtails navigate using sensors at the base of their antennae. They also release drops of their blood from pores to deter predators, since their blood is toxic or distasteful.
- In late winter, Hypogastruridae springtails, known as snow fleas, come to the surface of melting snow.
- A springtail that is 0.12–0.24" (3–6 mm) in size can leap 3–4" (75–100 mm).
- Springtails have a tube on their belly that they extend to soak up moisture, allowing them to survive when humidity falls, since they don't have a hard exoskeleton that prevents drying out.
- One species of springtail, *Cryptopygus antarcticus*, native to Australia and Antarctica, appeared on a postage stamp issued by the Falkland Island Dependencies.
- Some springtails can become wind-borne and disperse great distances. Some species can even be found on oceanic islands or coral atolls.
- Springtails preferentially fed on pathogenic fungi in a greenhouse setting, suggesting some could play a role in reducing plant stressors.

SPRINGTAILS

10. PROTURANS

CLASS: Protura » **ORDER:** Acerentomata » **FAMILIES:** Acerentomidae, Eosentomidae, Hesperentomidae, Protentomidae
SIZE: 0.024–0.098" (600μm–2.5 mm).
ECOLOGICAL ROLE: Proturans may play a secondary role in decomposition.
DESCRIPTION: Proturans are tiny, eyeless animals with pear-shaped heads and no visible mouthparts (mouthparts are internal). They are pale or yellow-brown in color. They have six legs but no antennae, and they walk on two pairs of legs and use their front legs as sensory organs, waving them back and forth in front of their body.
WHERE THEY ARE FOUND: Proturans live in moist soil, leaf litter, or in decaying wood, as well as under bark. They can penetrate deeper soil layers, up to nearly 10" (25.4 cm). They are absent in disturbed, degraded soils.
WHAT THEY EAT: Proturans consume algae and fungi, possibly also feeding on the mycorrhizae associated with tree roots.
LIFE CYCLE: Young proturans have nine segments in their abdomens and go through three molts; adults have 12 segments.
APPROX. NUMBER OF KNOWN SPECIES: 700 worldwide (80 in North America).
RELATIVE ABUNDANCE: Proturans are not often as abundant as other microarthropods but can occur in high numbers. Upper estimates range from 1,000 to 7,000 per square meter, and density appears to depend on organic matter. As many as five million may live on a single acre (85,000 per square meter).
NOTES OF INTEREST:

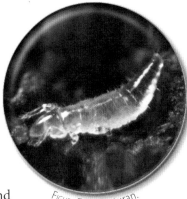

- When disturbed, proturans raise their abdomen in a defensive posture (like rove beetles or scorpions); they have a pair of defensive glands at the end of their abdomen that produce a repellent to help discourage predators.

- Proturans are a food source for mites, spiders, and pseudoscorpions.

FIGURE 70—Proturan.

11. DIPLURANS

CLASS: Diplura » **ORDER:** Dicellurata » **FAMILIES:** Campodeidae, Japygidae
SIZE: 0.079–0.79" (2–20 mm).
ECOLOGICAL ROLE: In soil food webs, diplurans are herbivores, detritivores, and predators.
DESCRIPTION: Diplurans have narrow, elongate bodies; an abdomen with 10 to 11 segments; and long, bead-like antennae. They are white or colorless. They have short legs and, at the end of their abdomen, two sensory appendages used for touch and smell, called cerci. Eyeless, their bodies are covered in sensory bristles. Diplurans in the family Campodeidae have filamentous cerci and are smaller and more delicate than other diplurans. Diplurans in the family Japygidae have pincerlike cerci at the end of their abdomens. Their wormlike body shape enables diplurans to travel in the interstitial system of the soil.
WHERE THEY ARE FOUND: Diplurans live in leaf litter, moss, rotting wood, and moist areas; on the surface of soil or within the soil up to depths of 4–8" (10–20 cm); and under bark or stones.
WHAT THEY EAT: Campodeids eat plant material, plants and animals that are decomposing, and fungal mycelia. Japygids eat small insects such as fly larvae, proturans, springtails, and nematodes.

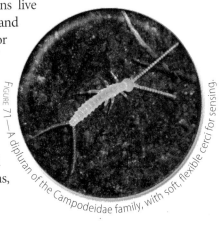

FIGURE 71—A dipluran of the Campodeidae family, with soft, flexible cerci for sensing.

FIGURE 72—A dipluran of the Japygidae family, with pincerlike cerci for sensing.

PROTURANS · DIPLURANS

LIFE CYCLE: Molting continues throughout their lives. Males deposit sperm in capsules on the ground that females pick up; females lay eggs in a mass or clump in cracks or in cavities in the ground.

APPROX. NUMBER OF KNOWN SPECIES: 800–1,000 worldwide (100 in North America).

RELATIVE ABUNDANCE: Diplurans are found in natural and human-modified soils, and they do not usually occur in high densities—approximately 50 per square meter.

NOTES OF INTEREST:

- Blind japygids detect prey using sensory hairs on their antennae—they grasp prey in their mouthparts before bending their abdomen over their head to seize prey with their pincers.
- Japygid females protect their eggs and larvae.
- Japygids are territorial and will make barriers to outline their boundaries.

12. BRISTLETAILS

CLASS: Insecta » **ORDER:** Microcoryphia
SIZE: 0.079–0.59" (2–15 mm).
ECOLOGICAL ROLE: Bristletails are scavengers in soil food webs, cleaning up plant and animal matter.
DESCRIPTION: Bristletails are wingless, with a humpback profile, long antennae, and large, compound eyes. Their bodies are covered with scales and are light gray to brown in color, and they have four long, taillike appendages.
WHERE THEY ARE FOUND: Bristletails occur in soil and leaf litter, in dead wood, under bark or dead wood, or under rocks.
WHAT THEY EAT: Bristletails feed at night on algae, fungi, plant detritus, decaying fruit, lichens, mosses, and dead arthropods.

FIGURE 73—Bristletail (*Archaeognatha* sp.) preparing to jump.

LIFE CYCLE: These insects have simple metamorphosis, and over the course of their lives lasting two to four years they may molt as many as 60 times. They attach themselves to a rock or stick using fecal material before they molt; if their cement fails before the molt is complete, they often do not survive the molting process. Females may mate every instar after their tenth, attaching their eggs to a substrate, like a rock.

APPROX. NUMBER OF KNOWN SPECIES: 350 worldwide (20 in North America).

RELATIVE ABUNDANCE: Bristletails do not usually occur in high densities—approaching 50 per square meter.

NOTES OF INTEREST:

- Bristletails have complex courtship rituals. After identifying mates using their antennae, males of some species place packages of sperm, called spermatophores, directly on a female, while males of other species spin a fine thread to which they attach their sperm packets and wait for the females to retrieve.
- Bristletails are fast runners and can jump randomly by arching their body and slapping their abdomen to fling to safety. They can jump as far as 12" (30 cm).
- Many bristletails are nocturnal, and their eyes glow at night in the beam of a flashlight.
- Bristletails are the closest living relatives to winged insects.

FIGURE 74—Bristletail (*Archaeognatha* sp.).

13. THRIPS

PHYLUM: Arthropoda » **CLASS:** Insecta » **ORDER:** Thysanoptera

SIZE: 0.02–0.2" (0.5–5 mm).

ECOLOGICAL ROLE: In the soil and leaf litter, thrips are fungivores or predators. Other thrips species are plant feeders and may act as vectors of plant diseases or damage agricultural crops.

DESCRIPTION: Thrips have small, slender, dark bodies and conical heads with piercing, sucking mouthparts and short antennae. Wings, when present, are long and very narrow with fringes of hairs.

WHERE THEY ARE FOUND: Thrips live in leaf litter, under bark, in decaying trees, and in fungi; non-soil-dwelling herbivorous thrips are found feeding on plants. About 50% of thrips species are found in leaf litter, in soil, or on fungi.

WHAT THEY EAT: Soil-dwelling and leaf-litter-dwelling thrips eat fungal spores, and others are predaceous on mites and small insects. Plant feeders eat leaves, fruits, flowers, and buds. Most ingest food in liquid form using their piercing, sucking mouthparts.

LIFE CYCLE: Parthenogenesis, a form of asexual reproduction, can occur in many species (females are diploid, and males are haploid, as in Hymenoptera). Females insert eggs into plant tissues or under bark. The first two instars, known as larvae, are feeding stages. The third and fourth instars are nonfeeding, inactive stages during which thrips are enclosed within a silk cocoon or cell made from soil and litter particles and undergo tissue rearrangements. This stage is called a pupa, though it is unlike the pupal stage of insects with complete metamorphosis. There are numerous generations in a growing season, with some species developing from egg to adult in as little as 10 days.

APPROX. NUMBER OF KNOWN SPECIES: 6,200 worldwide (700 in North America).

RELATIVE ABUNDANCE: Thrips can occur in large numbers but specific estimates of abundance in soil are not readily available.

FIGURE 75—Winged adult thrips.

FIGURE 76—Adult thrips with wing pads.

FIGURE 77—Wingless thrips species shown in multiple life stages.

NOTES OF INTEREST:

- Thrips' unique metamorphosis is somewhere between simple and complete: they have internal wing development as larvae (as occurs in complete metamorphosis), but also have external growth of wing pads that occurs before the adult stage (as occurs in simple metamorphosis).
- Some plant-feeding species of thrips are serious pests of cultivated plants (e.g., many in the family Thripidae).

- Thrips' tarsi have adhesive pads that enable them to cling to smooth surfaces.
- Winged and wingless species are dispersed long distances by wind.
- Thrips have asymmetric mouthparts.
- In American English usage, the singular form of thrips is the same as the plural.

THRIPS

14. EARTHWORMS

PHYLUM: Annelida » **CLASS:** Oligochaeta » **ORDER:** Opisthopora

SIZE: 0.39–15.7" (1–40 cm).

ECOLOGICAL ROLE: Earthworms are often the most familiar of the soil fauna, and they are also among the most important. Earthworms influence soil structure through their burrowing activities—some can burrow as deep as 8' (2.4 m)—and fragment and bury organic matter, mixing it with soil. Earthworm casts include minerals that are otherwise inaccessible to plant roots.

DESCRIPTION: Earthworms have soft, segmented, tubelike bodies. The anterior portion of the body houses the hearts, reproductive structures, and a mass of nerves, and this region can be recognized by the smooth, belt-like swelling near the front of the worm.

WHERE THEY ARE FOUND: Most often, earthworms are found in soil and leaf litter. Different species are found at different levels in the soil, with some living on the soil surface (epigeic), in topsoil (endogeic), or burrowed in deeper layers (anecic).

WHAT THEY EAT: Earthworms consume leaf litter and soil, including its minerals and organic matter.

LIFE CYCLE: All individuals have both male and female sex organs, and they exchange sperm during mating. Earthworm young develop within a cocoon in the soil and emerge looking like smaller adults. They reach maturity at around six weeks. Worms can live for four or more years.

APPROX. NUMBER OF KNOWN SPECIES: 7,260 worldwide (about 100 native to North America, plus approximately 45 introduced).

RELATIVE ABUNDANCE: On average, there are 100 to 500 earthworms per square meter, typically representing a large proportion of soil faunal biomass. Earthworms are less common in arid or acidic soils, with less than 10 per square meter, and more common in fertilized pastures, with more than 2,000 per square meter. Earthworms are most abundant in temperate and tropical forests and grasslands, and they're less diverse and abundant in deserts and polar regions.

NOTES OF INTEREST:

- Earthworm casts have about 50% more nutrients (calcium, nitrogen, phosphate, and potassium) and bacteria than surrounding soil. Earthworm casts also include calcium carbonate, a compound that lowers soil acidity.
- Worldwide, earthworms have been introduced through human activities (e.g., agriculture or

FIGURE 78—Native earthworm (*Eisenoides lonnbergi*).

FIGURE 79—Earthworm castings on soil.

EARTHWORMS

fishing). In the United States, some localities have all native species, some have all exotic species, and some have a mix.

- Forests are negatively impacted by nonnative earthworms, such as the Asian jumping worms (*Amynthas* and *Metaphire* spp.) found throughout the eastern and southern United States, as well as parts of the Midwest and Oregon. Jumping worms feed at the soil surface, consuming leaf litter and organic matter, and leaving behind worm castings that are depleted of nutrients and can't hold water. Asian jumping worms do not recycle and mix nutrients within the soil layers or create channels for plant roots. As jumping worms outcompete other worms, the resulting changes in soil structure reduce native plants and habitat and shelter for invertebrates, birds, amphibians, and other wildlife. Native earthworms are responsible for soil structure in the forests of the Pacific Northwest.

- A few native species in the United States can reach a foot in length or even more. The giant Palouse earthworm (*Driloleirus americanus*) can be up to 3.28' (1 m) or more in length, though modern specimens have been smaller. Note: this species is thought to be in decline, and few individuals have been found in the decade beginning in 2010.

- Charles Darwin devoted his last book, *The Formation of Vegetable Mould, Through the Action of Worms* (1881), to earthworms. He wrote, "It may be doubted whether there are many other animals which have played so important a part in the history of the world, as have these lowly organised creatures."

- Darwin observed that earthworms could learn and adapt their behaviors based on their experiences. For example, he noted that they figured out which part of a leaf to pull on to most successfully get the leaf into their burrow.

- Earthworms have the ability to regenerate some lost segments, though this is not well understood.

- Tillage, along with pesticides, can reduce the density of earthworms or remove them entirely. Long-term agronomic trials, including some trials in operation for more than 170 years, have found significant declines (50–100%) in earthworm biomass under intensive agricultural management. However, degraded soils converted to conservation management often show an increase in earthworm densities.

- In Australia, earthworms in the genus *Megascolides* can reach lengths of 9' (2.7 m).

FIGURE 80—Asian jumping worm (*Amynthas agrestis*).

- Hand digging and sorting is a common sampling method for earthworms. Mustard extraction—which involves pouring a mix of water and mustard powder over a plot of earth and counting the number of earthworms, whose skin is irritated by the mustard, that rise to the surface—can also be very effective.

FIGURE 81—Common nightcrawler (*Lumbricus terrestris*).

FIGURE 82—A significant negative impact of nightcrawler infestation is the removal of organic residues from the surface into the mineral layers of soil. Without the protection of leaf litter, the soil surface is dryer, warmer and poorer habitat for other plants and animals.

15. SLUGS AND SNAILS

PHYLUM: Mollusca » **CLASS:** Gastropoda
SIZE: 0.059–4.7" (1.5 mm–12 cm).

ECOLOGICAL ROLE: Snails and slugs are decomposers and scavengers, and they are particularly important in moist ecosystems. Some species are predators. Snails are important in calcium cycling, concentrating calcium in their shells. Snails are important food sources for wildlife, passing calcium further into the food web as they are eaten by predators.

DESCRIPTION: Snails and slugs are soft-bodied animals with one or two pairs of retractable tentacles on their heads (their eyes are on the uppermost tentacles) and a strong, muscular foot. Their foot is coated in a slimy layer of mucus that reduces moisture loss and helps them to traverse rough surfaces. Slugs and snails use a radula, a structure with rows of teeth, to scrape food from surfaces. Snails carry a shell enriched with calcium on their back, and some species can retract their body inside the shell.

WHERE THEY ARE FOUND: Land slugs and snails are found in leaf litter and soil, at the base of grasses and sedges, and under logs, the bark of dead trees, and rocks. Slugs can sometimes live in places snails cannot because they have no shell and therefore have fewer calcium requirements. Slugs and snails don't disperse readily, but they are moved frequently through human activities (such as the importation of food and plants, and the transport of soil, logs, and plants), and there are a number of introduced species in the United States.

WHAT THEY EAT: Slugs and snails feed on fungi, decaying plant matter, feces, carrion, and fresh plant material. Predatory snails and slugs feed on earthworms, potworms, and other snails or slugs.

LIFE CYCLE: Slugs and snails lay eggs in clusters in moist places, such as under logs or leaf litter. Newly hatched young are small versions of adults, though young slugs often have lighter, different color patterns, and young snails have nearly translucent shells. Slugs reach maturity between three to nine months, and all are hermaphroditic, mutually exchanging sperm during mating. Many species die after egg laying. Snails may live for a few months, but some take longer to mature and may live for four or more years. Slug and snail activity depends on the season—in winter and dry, hot summer weather, species burrow under soil or logs and are inactive.

FIGURE 83—Slugs can cause economic damage to soybean and other row crops, particularly when insecticide-treated seeds kill off the natural insect predators of slugs.

FIGURE 84—Invasive European Arionidae species can be pests of various row crops—like lettuce.

FIGURE 85—The predatory rosy wolfsnail (*Euglandina rosea*), native to the southern United States, eats other snails.

FIGURE 86—Snails engaging in a courtship dance.

FIGURE 87—Common garden slug (*Deroceras reticulatum*) laying eggs.

APPROX. NUMBER OF KNOWN SPECIES: 30,000 land snails and 500 land slugs worldwide (1,100 native snails and 40 native slugs in North America).

RELATIVE ABUNDANCE: In North America, native slugs are not typically abundant under natural conditions. Introduced species can become locally abundant.

NOTES OF INTEREST:

- Gastropod is derived from the Greek words for belly (*gastros*) and foot (*podos*), and indeed these animals do travel on their bellies.
- Land snails are food for beetles, millipedes, other snails; parasitic mites, nematodes, and flies; and salamanders, turtles, small mammals, and birds.
- Snails don't move very far during their lives and can be indicators of habitat conditions or pollution (e.g., they take up toxic cadmium).
- Land snails are a food source for people, though some snails can be hosts to mammalian parasites.
- Introduced species of snails and slugs cause a host of ecological problems; slugs from the family Arionidae are significant pests in the eastern United States, and *Theba pisana* is an ornamental and crop pest in California. There are many species of slugs that have been introduced in the United States (e.g., the Northeast has three native slug species and 13 introduced species). There are at least 70 species of nonnative snails in the United States.

- The majority of land snails have lungs but a few have gills, and these species usually live in very damp places.
- The foot of snails and slugs moves by successive, wavelike contractions.
- The trails of snails and slugs have chemical components that can attract mates and predators, and repel competitors.
- Banana slugs (*Ariolimax*), found in the Pacific Northwest, are important members of forest communities.
- Slug slime can absorb lots of water (one estimate: 100 times its original weight).
- Slugs and snails have courtship displays, with some that include a dance.

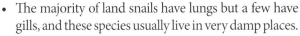

FIGURE 88—Native banana slug (*Ariolimax* sp.) eggs and hatchlings.

FIGURE 89—Slender banana slug (*Ariolimax dolichophallus*) eating a *Russula* mushroom.

16. WOODLICE (SOWBUGS AND PILLBUGS)

PHYLUM: Arthropoda » **SUBPHYLUM:** Crustacea » **CLASS:** Malacostraca » **ORDER:** Isopoda » **SUBORDER:** Oniscidea
SIZE: 0.2–0.59" (5–15 mm).

ECOLOGICAL ROLE: Woodlice are primary decomposers and contribute significantly to decomposition by fragmenting fresh plant debris, which allows mites, springtails, potworms, and bacteria to continue the process of forming humus. As detritivores, they can also further break down overwintered leaves and plant material that has been degraded by microorganisms.

DESCRIPTION: These terrestrial crustaceans have gray or brown bodies that are segmented and have the appearance of armor. They have powerful biting mouthparts used to fragment plant debris, seven pairs of legs, and two pairs of antennae. Pillbugs (family Armadillidiidae) can roll into a ball. Sowbugs (family Porcellionidae) do not roll their bodies into a ball, and they have two noticeable short, taillike appendages called uropods on their hind end.

WHERE THEY ARE FOUND: Woodlice occur underneath logs, stones, and bark, and in moist leaf litter. Seasonal activity of woodlice is dependent on moisture and temperature. On cool, damp days in autumn, they are active in newly fallen leaves. In warm, dry summers, they remain in the upper soil layers and are mainly nocturnal.

WHAT THEY EAT: Woodlice are scavengers of plant material, feeding on decayed or soft matter like leaf litter. Some also feed on roots or seedlings. Many species have preferences for consuming certain leaf species.

LIFE CYCLE: Females carry eggs underneath their body, and young feed on fluid from their mother. Young molt every one to two weeks for four to five months before reaching the adult stage. Adults can live for two or more years.

APPROX. NUMBER OF KNOWN SPECIES: 3,000 worldwide (72 native to North America and 27 introduced).

RELATIVE ABUNDANCE: High in moist, temperate areas, there can be 100 to 600 per square meter.

FIGURE 90—Common rough woodlouse (*Porcellio scaber*).

FIGURE 91—Pillbug in leaf litter.

FIGURE 92—Pillbug curled into defensive ball.

NOTES OF INTEREST:

- Many woodlice in North America, including all pillbugs, are introduced species, originally from Europe.
- They have symbiotic bacteria in their gut that help to break down their nutrient-poor diets.
- They also eat dung from other woodlice because it contains copper, an element needed by their blood but uncommon on land. Copper is more abundant in the oceans inhabited by their marine relatives.

- Pillbugs are often known as roly-polies, due to their ability to roll into a tight ball as a defense mechanism. Woodlice have many common names: armadillobug, doodlebug, peabug, gramersow, and more.
- Woodlice significantly prefer freshly fallen leaves; some species may have secondary preferences for types of foliage (e.g., holly over oak).

17. CRAYFISH

PHYLUM: Arthropoda » **CLASS:** Malacostraca » **ORDER:** Decapoda » **SUPERFAMILY:** Astacidea

SIZE: 1–6" (2–16 cm).

ECOLOGICAL ROLE: In soil food webs, crayfish are decomposers and predators. They are important movers and mixers of moist soil, contributing to soil turnover in poorly drained soils that are less frequented by other soil movers like earthworms.

DESCRIPTION: Like other arthropods, crayfish have a hard exoskeleton that protects their body. They have beady eyes, two pairs of antennae, four pairs of walking legs, and one pair of legs with pincers used for feeding, defense, burrowing, and mating. Crayfish have a jointed abdomen and a fan-shaped tail. Many crayfish are brown or green, but some are red, blue, black, or white.

WHERE THEY ARE FOUND: Crayfish are found in burrows in moist soils, such as those in low-lying fields or forests. Crayfish burrows are as deep as the water table—the level at which soils are fully saturated—which can be up to 16.4" (5 m) deep. On the soil surface, chimneys made from excavated earth are a sign of crayfish burrowing activity; they are rarely seen above ground during the day. They also live in freshwater streams, ponds, marshes, and lakes.

WHAT THEY EAT: Crayfish eat living and dead plants; prey upon insects, snails, tadpoles, and fish; and also consume dead animal matter. Most crayfish feed at night.

LIFE CYCLE: Crayfish often mate in autumn, and female crayfish lay fertilized eggs in the spring, gluing them to the underside of her abdomen to incubate. After hatching, young crayfish remain near their mother for several months. Some species reach maturity within a year and others in two, and typical life spans are between two and four years.

APPROX. NUMBER OF KNOWN SPECIES: 500 worldwide (405 in North America).

RELATIVE ABUNDANCE: Crayfish are typically not abundant but can become so in years with excessive rain or in areas where the water table is raised artificially, such as rice fields.

NOTES OF INTEREST:

- Crayfish can bring more than one ton of soil to the surface per acre of land per year.
- Crayfish are critical food sources for mammals, birds, and fish. Crayfish are trapped and are eaten by people as well.
- They are important in aquatic food chains, contributing to decomposition of plants and animals.
- Because they are sensitive to pesticides and heavy metals, crayfish are indicators of water quality.
- There are four species listed under the Endangered Species Act and nearly 50 species protected at the state level. Some researchers estimate that about 48% of crayfish species are imperiled. A number of species have a limited geographic range, which can make them more vulnerable.
- Nonnative crayfish are a threat to aquatic biodiversity, contributing to the decline of native crayfish and negatively impacting native fish and aquatic plants.
- There is considerable regional variation in names for this freshwater arthropod. Common names in the United States also include crawfish, crawdads, and mudbugs.

FIGURE 93—Crayfish emerging from a burrow.

FIGURE 94—A collar of excavated soil surrounding the opening of the burrow is a sign of crayfish.

CRAYFISH

18. MILLIPEDES

PHYLUM: Arthropoda » **SUBPHYLUM:** Myriapoda » **CLASS:** Diplopoda

SIZE: 0.079–11" (2–280 mm) but most are 2–2.4" (5–6 cm).

ECOLOGICAL ROLE: Millipedes are primary decomposers and scavengers, and they make significant contributions to the decomposition of plant debris. Millipedes fragment 10–15% of annual leaf fall and facilitate further microbial decomposition.

DESCRIPTION: Millipedes have an elongated, segmented body with many legs—up to 375 pairs. Each body segment has two pairs of legs. They have one pair of antennae and lack structures to bite people, but they do have mandibles for chewing organic matter. Millipedes are often black, brown, or gray, and sometimes with bright, colorful legs or patterns.

WHERE THEY ARE FOUND: Millipedes occur in all subarctic environments except deserts, but they primarily occur in moist habitats. They live under bark, logs, and stones, and in leaf litter and upper soil layers. Some can excavate deep tunnels and are found in deep soil layers. Millipedes are not fast runners but are powerful diggers.

WHAT THEY EAT: Millipedes eat debris—decaying vegetation like fallen leaves, algae, and fungi. They are selective feeders, preferring leaf litter with high calcium and avoiding freshly fallen leaves.

LIFE CYCLE: Millipedes have a life span up to 11 years. A female millipede covers her eggs in a ball made of soil particles and droppings and places them in a nest, which she guards. When millipedes molt, they create their own nests for shelter during the process.

APPROX. NUMBER OF KNOWN SPECIES: 12,000 worldwide (915 in North America).

RELATIVE ABUNDANCE: In temperate regions, there can be 10 to more than 100 individuals per square meter, but millipedes can be especially abundant in temperate forests, with numbers up to 1,000 per square meter.

NOTES OF INTEREST:

- Millipedes in the genus *Motyxia* are bioluminescent, helping to warn off potential predators.
- One defense mechanism is to roll into a ball or a coil. Pill millipedes, in the superorder Oniscomorpha, take this to a whole other level, enclosing their head, legs, and more.
- Defensive secretions either smell terrible or contain toxic substances.
- Their droppings contribute to humus and soil formation.
- When the soil is too hard, millipedes in the family Iulidae (alternative spelling of Julidae) eat their way through.

FIGURE 95—Millipede.

FIGURE 96—Millipedes have two pairs of legs for each body segment.

FIGURE 97—American giant millipede (*Narceus americanus*) in defensive position.

- Millipede means "thousand feet" but none are known to actually have 1,000 legs (the maximum is 750, in *Illacme plenipes*, which is also the animal with the most legs).

- The largest millipede in the world, *Archispirostreptus gigas*, known as the giant African millipede, is more than 15" (38.1 cm) long and can live up to seven years.

19. CENTIPEDES

PHYLUM: Arthropoda » **SUBPHYLUM:** Myriapoda » **CLASS:** Chilopoda

SIZE: 0.12–11.8" (3–300 mm).

ECOLOGICAL ROLE: In soil food webs, centipedes are predators. Some are also detritivores.

DESCRIPTION: Centipedes have elongated, flattened, segmented bodies with one pair of legs per body segment. They have long antennae, and their first pair of walking legs are modified to inject prey with venom.

WHERE THEY ARE FOUND: Some species are adapted to live in shallow or deep soil layers, while others live under bark, logs, and stones, or within leaf litter. Most species are nocturnal and more often seen at night.

WHAT THEY EAT: Centipedes eat earthworms and other arthropods, large and small (they are fast runners and will chase prey). Larger species may also prey on small mammals or reptiles. Centipedes immobilize prey by injecting it with poison, and will then tear open prey, cover it in digestive fluids, and suck out the contents. Some species will also eat plant debris on occasion.

LIFE CYCLE: Males have mating displays. Some species lay single eggs in soil, while females of other species provide parental care for a nest of eggs in soil or rotten wood. Young of some species start out with a few body segments and pairs of legs and add the rest as they grow and molt, while the young of others start out with the number of legs and segments they'll have as adults and grow in size through molting. It can take several years for centipedes to reach adulthood, and they are relatively long-lived, with lives up to six years.

APPROX. NUMBER OF KNOWN SPECIES: 3,000 worldwide (40 in North America).

RELATIVE ABUNDANCE: Data unavailable.

NOTES OF INTEREST:

- Female centipedes guard eggs, licking them to reduce fungal infections.
- Many centipedes are fast runners, and larger species can bite people if handled.
- The largest species, *Scolopendra gigantea*, occurring in South America, is among the world's largest terrestrial invertebrates and largest invertebrate carnivores.

FIGURE 98—Centipede on soil.

FIGURE 99—Centipede burrowing into soil.

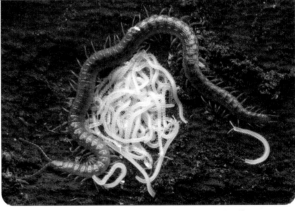
FIGURE 100—Soil centipede (*Geophilus* sp.) mother with offspring.

MILLIPEDES • CENTIPEDES

20. SPIDERS

PHYLUM: Arthropoda » **CLASS:** Arachnida » **ORDER:** Araneae » **FAMILIES:** Agelenidae, Atypidae, Clubionidae, Gnaphosidae, Hahniidae, Lycosidae, Salticidae

SIZE: 0.079–1.18" (2–30 mm).

ECOLOGICAL ROLE: As predators that either hunt down prey or spin complex webs to trap prey, spiders help regulate arthropod populations. As diggers, they also move and work the soil.

DESCRIPTION: Spiders have four pairs of walking legs and two body regions, known as the cephalothorax (the head and thorax combined) and the abdomen. Silk-spinning organs are found at the posterior end of the abdomen. Most spiders have eight eyes, the arrangement of which can help identify spider groups. The spiders use their jaws, called chelicerae, to hold prey and inject poison or to help burrow into soil.

HUNTING SPIDERS THAT ARE SEEN MOST OFTEN: Wolf spiders (Lycosidae) have brown, black, or dirty-yellow coloration, often with one or more longitudinal stripes on their backs. Jumping spiders (Salticidae) have variable body coloration, usually dark with iridescent patterns, a fuzzy appearance, and large, forward-facing eyes. Ground spiders (Gnaphosidae) are dark and drab with prominent spinnerets.

WHERE THEY ARE FOUND: Web-building spiders, such as dwarf sheet spiders (Hahniidae), sac spiders (Clubionidae), or funnel weavers (Agelenidae), are found within webs spun in or directly on the ground. These webs may be domes, funnels, tubes, or simple sheets across the surface. For example, purseweb spiders (Atypidae) construct deep, vertical tubes of silk and wait to ambush insects from below, pulling them into the tunnel. Hunting spiders, such as wolf spiders, ground spiders, or jumping spiders, are all found on the soil surface or in leaf litter.

WHAT THEY EAT: Spiders eat other arthropods, including many insects.

LIFE CYCLE: Spiders may lay eggs within silken sacs in leaf litter, attached to their web, or attached to their body. Adults or eggs overwinter in silken nests in soil, grass clumps, and leaf litter; under bark; or inside hollow stalks of vegetation. Most spiders have one generation a year. Adults can live for one to three years.

APPROX. NUMBER OF KNOWN SPECIES: 2,430 wolf spiders worldwide (240 in North America), 6,175 jumping spiders worldwide (315 in North America), 1,330 funnel weavers worldwide (116 in North America), 54 purseweb spiders worldwide (eight in North America), 630 sac spiders worldwide (58 in North America), 350 dwarf sheet spiders worldwide (58 in North America), and 2,520 ground spiders worldwide (180 in North America).

RELATIVE ABUNDANCE: Spiders can be fairly abundant. In woodland soil, spider populations were estimated at 50 to 150 per square meter; similarly, 142 spiders per square meter were found in an English pasture.

NOTES OF INTEREST:

- Spiders have fangs on the tips of their chelicerae, and the venom within contains toxins and enzymes used to stun or kill prey and also helps to speed up digestion of prey body tissues.
- Spiders provide maternal care for their young. Wolf spiders carry their young (up to 100) on their back, and funnel weavers stay in their mother's web for weeks. Some mothers provide regurgitated food as well.

FIGURE 101—Wolf spider.

FIGURE 102—Ground spider (*Herpyllus ecclesiasticus*).

SPIDERS

FIGURE 103—Jumping spider with plant bug prey.

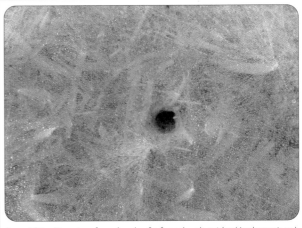
FIGURE 104—Signature funnel web of a funnel web spider (*Agelenopsis* sp.).

- Sheetweb spiders (Linyphiidae) tend to catch more flying insects, and their contribution to soil health is mainly the byproducts of their meals.
- Jumping spiders always attach a safety thread before leaping.
- A group of wafer-lid trapdoor spiders (Euctenizidae) is found in the southern United States.
- Spiders are fairly territorial and have complicated mating rituals.

- Spider populations can be disrupted by planting and harvesting of crops, but they can recolonize fields if suitable habitats such as natural areas or permanently planted field borders are nearby. Greater numbers of spiders are found in no-till or reduced tillage systems.
- Pitfall traps capture spiders, and Berlese funnels are also useful for sampling.

21. HARVESTMEN

PHYLUM: Arthropoda » CLASS: Arachnida »
  ORDER: Opiliones » SUPERFAMILY: Phalangioidea
SIZE: 0.079–0.47" (2–12 mm).
ECOLOGICAL ROLE: Harvestmen are predators on the soil surface and also can fill the roles of decomposers, scavengers, and herbivores.
DESCRIPTION: Harvestmen have two body regions that are broadly joined and appear as one round body. Their oval bodies may have gray, brown, or tan color patterns. They have eight exceptionally long, stilt-like legs, using the second pair of legs to search for prey and sense their environment. These arachnids have chelicerae but do not have venom glands, do not have silk glands, and have only two eyes.
WHERE THEY ARE FOUND: Harvestmen can be found on the soil surface or in leaf litter in gardens, field edges, grasslands, and woodlands.

FIGURE 105—Polished harvestman (*Leiobunum politum*) adult female, preying on an earthworm.

WHAT THEY EAT: Harvestmen feed on a variety of arthropods and snails, and they are active during the day as well as during dawn and dusk. Some are omnivorous and will feed on dead plant or animal material.
LIFE CYCLE: Eggs overwinter after they are laid in soil or leaf litter in late summer and autumn. Juveniles reach maturity in the late spring or summer, depending on climate. Harvestmen lay one generation per year, and most species only live for a year.

SPIDERS • HARVESTMEN

APPROX. NUMBER OF KNOWN SPECIES: 6,600 worldwide (150 in North America).

RELATIVE ABUNDANCE: Data unavailable.

NOTES OF INTEREST:

- Harvestmen are also known as daddy longlegs.
- A common urban legend suggests that harvestmen have potent venom but mouthparts too small to bite humans. In fact, they are not venomous, and their chelicerae are more suited for grasping than biting.
- Harvestmen use their second pair of legs to detect odors of food or mates, and they will preen these legs to keep them clean.
- These arachnids have stink glands and will secrete a foul substance to deter predators. Harvestmen will also break off pieces of legs if an enemy seizes it (the leg cannot be regenerated).
- Harvestmen are often a vehicle for pseudoscorpions or mites that hitch a ride to disperse further.
- Tillage can harm harvestmen populations.

Figure 106—Harvestmen with mites.

22. PSEUDOSCORPIONS

PHYLUM: Arthropoda » **CLASS:** Arachnida » **ORDER:** Pseudoscorpiones

SIZE: 0.079–0.28" (2–7 mm).

ECOLOGICAL ROLE: Pseudoscorpions are predators, regulating populations of mesofauna of the soil.

DESCRIPTION: Pseudoscorpions have conspicuous, large appendages called pedipalps, which end in strong pincers used to capture prey or for defense. In this way, they resemble scorpions, but they do not have a tail with a stinger at the end. They have two main body regions: the cephalothorax includes the head and appendages (chelicerae, pedipalps, and four pairs of walking legs), and the abdomen has 11 to 12 segments without any appendages. Some have simple eyes, while others are blind.

WHERE THEY ARE FOUND: Pseudoscorpions inhabit the soil, including in ant or ground-nesting bee nests, and are also found in leaf litter and under logs, stones, or bark.

WHAT THEY EAT: Pseudoscorpions hunt and immobilize springtails, mites, nematodes, potworms, and larval soil arthropods using their venom.

LIFE CYCLE: Pseudoscorpions spin silken chambers in which they molt and overwinter. They can live up to three to four years. A female pseudoscorpion will carry a silken bag of 10 to 40 eggs, and her young will ride on her for a time after they hatch.

APPROX. NUMBER OF KNOWN SPECIES: 3,500 worldwide (420 in North America).

RELATIVE ABUNDANCE: Pseudoscorpions are not present in high density, with less than 300 per square meter.

NOTES OF INTEREST:

- Pseudoscorpions' chelicerae are used for feeding and for producing silk.
- Sensory hairs on their pedipalps help detect prey.
- Some pseudoscorpions hitch rides on insects as a method of dispersal.
- These animals can be sampled using a Berlese funnel.

Figure 107—Pseudoscorpion with psocid prey.

Figure 108—Pseudoscorpions catching a ride on a larger insect's leg.

Figure 109—Pseudoscorpion female carrying eggs.

23. SCORPIONS

PHYLUM: Arthropoda » **CLASS:** Arachnida » **ORDERS:** Amblypygi, Schizomida, Scorpiones, Solifugae, Thelyphonida
SIZE: 0.31–6.69" (8 mm–17 cm).
ECOLOGICAL ROLE: Scorpions are predators, feeding on a variety of small animals. Most scorpions are also burrowers, digging several feet underground.

DESCRIPTION: All scorpions have segmented bodies, eight legs, a pair of chelicerae, and a pair of pedipalps. True scorpions (Scorpiones) have a tail ending in a venomous stinger, often carried over their back, and pedipalps ending in pincers. Wind scorpions (Solifugae) have a rounded abdomen and no stinger, with large pedipalps used to seize prey. Wind scorpions, whip scorpions (Thelyphonida), tailless whip scorpions (Amblypygi), and short-tailed whip scorpions (Schizomida) run on their three hind legs and use the front pair of legs as feelers. Whip scorpions resemble true scorpions but have a long, thin tail. Tailless whip scorpions have very long legs, no tail, and pedipalps modified for grabbing. Short-tailed whip scorpions have hind legs modified for jumping and a short tail extending from their abdomen.

FIGURE 110—Common striped scorpion.

WHERE THEY ARE FOUND: Scorpions are found in hot, dry climates. Some true scorpions, as well as whip scorpions and short-tailed whip scorpions, also live in warm and humid climates. They can be found in soil, under logs or stones, or within burrows of larger animals.

WHAT THEY EAT: Scorpions are nocturnal hunters and emerge at night to feed on insects, centipedes, spiders, and other arachnids, as well as small vertebrates like mice, lizards, and snakes. Prey selection can be varied; up to 100 prey species were recorded for one scorpion species. Some scorpions can survive a whole year without food.

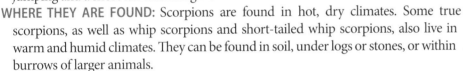

FIGURE 111—Short-tailed whipscorpion (Hubbardia sp.).

LIFE CYCLE: True scorpions birth live young and carry their young on their back for several weeks. Adult females of other scorpions also provide maternal care. Some species may dig deep burrows underground where they lay eggs. Others may carry eggs in sacs on their abdomens or stay in a chamber with their eggs until they hatch. Scorpions grow slowly and may take several years to reach maturity. They may live three to 10 years, or even up to 15 years.

APPROX. NUMBER OF KNOWN SPECIES: 1,950 true scorpions worldwide (70 in North America), 1,100 wind scorpions worldwide (200 in North America), 100 whip scorpions worldwide (three in North America), 150 tailless whip scorpions worldwide (nine in North America), and 230 short-tailed whip scorpions worldwide (60 in North America).

RELATIVE ABUNDANCE: Scorpions are not numerous.

NOTES OF INTEREST:

- True scorpions have a venomous sting but only about 1.5% of species pose a health risk to people. In the United States, the Arizona bark scorpion, *Centruroides sculpturatus*, is considered seriously dangerous to people; scorpion stings are avoidable by wearing shoes outdoors where scorpions are present and by shaking out shoes and clothes if they've been on the floor before wearing.
- There are 75 or so species of true scorpions in the United States, and the highest diversity is in the desert Southwest (e.g., there are 40 species in Arizona).
- True scorpions have both a type of venom to stun or warn predators or threats, and a type for killing prey.
- Wind scorpions (also called camel spiders) don't have poison glands. Whip scorpions, which have no venom glands, spray acetic acid in defense.
- *Scorpius* is the only constellation of stars to bear the name of a soil organism, and it is one of two named for arthropods (the other is Cancer, the crab).
- The exoskeleton of scorpions will fluoresce under black light, so surveys can be conducted at nighttime.

SCORPIONS

> **INSECTS: CLASS INSECTA** includes a great number of insect orders that dwell in the soil for all or a portion of their life cycle or that are involved in soil food webs, including all of the most diverse groups (e.g., beetles, flies, bees, wasps, ants, butterflies, and moths). These insects are important predators, root feeders, modifiers of soil structure, or decomposers.

MACROFAUNA » INSECTS

24. SILVERFISH

PHYLUM: Arthropoda » CLASS: Insecta »
ORDER: Zygentoma

SIZE: 0.39–0.59" (10–15 mm).

ECOLOGICAL ROLE: Silverfish are decomposers, but the extent of their ecological role is not fully understood.

DESCRIPTION: Silverfish are wingless, with flat, wide bodies covered in silvery scales. They are brown or gray in color. Eyes are small or absent, but they have long antennae and long, taillike appendages.

WHERE THEY ARE FOUND: Silverfish live in leaf litter, under stones, or underground in mammal burrows and ant and termite nests; they also can live in buildings.

WHAT THEY EAT: Silverfish eat decaying vegetation and starchy substances.

FIGURE 112—Small blue silverfish (*Lepisma saccharina*).

LIFE CYCLE: These insects have simple metamorphosis without much noticeable change between molts. They have life spans of two to four years and have complex courtship routines.

APPROX. NUMBER OF KNOWN SPECIES: 370 worldwide (18 in North America).

RELATIVE ABUNDANCE: Silverfish are sensitive to moisture and are not abundant if humidity is low.

NOTES OF INTEREST:

- These insects are rapid runners.
- Some species that live inside dwellings eat book bindings, wallpaper paste, clothing, and more.
- Silverfish have water-absorbing vesicles on their underside for quick uptake of water from their environment.

25. COCKROACHES

PHYLUM: Arthropoda » CLASS: Insecta » ORDER: Blattodea » FAMILIES: Blaberidae, Blattidae, Ectobiidae

SIZE: 0.12–1.97" (3–50 mm).

ECOLOGICAL ROLE: Cockroaches are decomposers and scavengers in leaf litter and on the soil surface.

DESCRIPTION: Soil-dwelling cockroaches are adapted to life in leaf litter, with their brown-and-black flattened, oval bodies; a head that is concealed by their thorax; and legs that can be tucked in close. Their threadlike antennae are very long—at least half as long (but typically nearly as long as) their bodies. Stout, bristled taillike appendages called cerci help them detect slight movements nearby.

WHERE THEY ARE FOUND: Soil-dwelling cockroaches are found in the upper soil layer and litter layer, and under logs.

FIGURE 113—Wood-eating cockroach (*Cryptocercus kybeanensis*).

SILVERFISH

COCKROACHES

WHAT THEY EAT: Cockroaches are omnivorous, feeding on rotting plants and detritus. They are mainly nocturnal.

LIFE CYCLE: Cockroaches enclose eggs in a capsule, called an ootheca, which is either carried by the female or left in litter. Nymphal development ranges from several months to more than a year, and adults can be long-lived, up to four years or more.

APPROX. NUMBER OF KNOWN SPECIES: 4,500 worldwide (50 in the United States).

RELATIVE ABUNDANCE: Cockroaches have relatively low population densities.

NOTES OF INTEREST:

- Their antennae have tactile and olfactory receptors, as well as humidity and temperature receptors. When they are exploring, they move their antennae in continuous, circular movements to help them detect things in the near vicinity.
- Cockroaches of the genus *Cryptocercus* feed on wood within decaying logs and have internal mutualistic microbes that help them break down cellulose. Mated pairs of cockroaches live within their logs providing care for up to 20 nymphs. Raising brood together over several years, the parental care that males and females provide together for offspring is unusual for insects. In the United States, four species of *Cryptocercus* are found in eastern states and one species is found in the West.
- *Attaphila* cockroaches, found in the United States only in Texas and Louisiana, live within nests of leaf-cutter ants (*Atta*) and eat the fungus cultivated on leaf tissue chewed by the ants.

FIGURE 114—Female cockroach deposits a mass of eggs in an ootheca.

- Cockroaches play a more minor role in soil biology since they are typically in low population densities.

26. TERMITES

PHYLUM: Arthropoda » **CLASS:** Insecta » **ORDER:** Blattodea » **FAMILIES:** Kalotermitidae, Rhinotermitidae, Termitidae

SIZE: 0.08–0.8" (2–20 mm).

ECOLOGICAL ROLE: As major ecosystem engineers and decomposers that transform soil structure and clean up plant litter, termites are among the most important soil fauna. Their work recycles wood and plants, and aerates and enriches soils with nutrients.

DESCRIPTION: Termites have soft bodies that are usually light in color. Their abdomen is broadly joined to the thorax, and they have a broad head with simple threadlike antennae. Their role in the colony determines their appearance: Reproductive individuals have eyes and wings, queens tend to have very large abdomens, and shed their wings after swarming to establish a new colony. Most workers and soldiers are blind and have chewing mouthparts. Soldiers have larger, dark, hard heads with powerful mandibles used in defense.

WHERE THEY ARE FOUND: Termites live in highly organized colonies in the soil and within dead wood.

FIGURE 115—Winged termite males.
FIGURE 116—A termite queen (center), surrounded by workers.
FIGURE 117—A reproductive termite after shedding wings.
FIGURE 118—Soldier with workers and nymphs.

TERMITES

WHAT THEY EAT: Termites feed on some of the least nutritious and indigestible foods: decaying plant material. They must eat huge quantities of leaf litter, grass, dead wood, and twigs in order to survive. Microbes in their guts help termites digest cellulose; these microbes are shared through the transfer of regurgitated liquids and through feeding on droppings of fellow termites.

LIFE CYCLE: Termite colonies are established by one king and queen that initiate reproduction. Queens can be long-lived—up to 15 years or more—and once colonies reach a certain size, queens can lay 1,000 to 3,000 eggs per day. In the early stages of colony formation, kings and queens rear workers, feeding them predigested food until they can feed themselves. Younger nymphs and workers then take over rearing and other duties. Workers go on to construct galleries and forage for food, while soldiers defend the colony. Workers and soldiers can live up to four years. Reproductive individuals disperse from established colonies to colonize new locations.

APPROX. NUMBER OF KNOWN SPECIES: 3,000 worldwide (47 in the United States).

RELATIVE ABUNDANCE: Termites are found in large numbers in warmer parts of the world and are at their highest densities in tropical rainforests, where there can be 10,000 per square meter.

NOTES OF INTEREST:

- Termites can communicate with each other through tactile signals and with pheromones.
- Termites are "social cockroaches." Though their social system resembles that of ants (termites have been popularly referred to as "white ants"), termites are closely related to cockroaches.
- In the United States, a few termite species are considered structural pests or pests of timber.
- In grasslands of Arizona, termites clear up to 92% of the plant litter, which works out to about 400 lb. (181 kg) of plant material per acre of ground.
- A number of arthropods occur in termite nests: mites, ants, springtails, beetles, and centipedes all share space with termites.
- In Africa, South America, and Australia, some species build large mounds in the shape of pyramids or turrets. Thirty mounds may occupy one acre, and 5,000 tons of soil may be moved during the construction of those mounds, an astounding amount for such small animals.
- In the tropics, termites cultivate fungi on their droppings and consume those fungi.

FIGURE 119—Subterranean termite mound. with extensive shelter tubes aboveground for colony protection.

FIGURE 120—Termite workers constructing shelter tubes above an underground nest.

FIGURE 121—Turret-shaped Australian termite mound.

- Termites are an important food source for a variety of birds and mammals.
- Queen termites have the longest lifespans of insects, with queens living beyond 20 years.
- The distribution and diversity of termites is greatest in the southern hemisphere.

27. EARWIGS

PHYLUM: Arthropoda » **CLASS:** Insecta » **ORDER:** Dermaptera » **FAMILIES:** Forficulidae, Labiduridae
SIZE: 0.24–0.8" (6–20 mm).
ECOLOGICAL ROLE: In food webs, earwigs are decomposers, herbivores, and predators, and they move and mix soil when they burrow.

DESCRIPTION: Earwigs have a slender and elongated body that is smooth and leathery. They lack simple eyes, called ocelli, and some species also lack compound eyes. Earwigs can be winged or wingless. They have particularly hardened, pincer- or forceps-like sensory appendages, called cerci, which are used in defense, prey capture, and courtship. In earwigs with wings, the front wings are short and leathery, and they do not fully cover the hind wings or abdomen (similar in that respect to rove beetles).

WHERE THEY ARE FOUND: Earwigs are active at night in leaf litter, and they hide during the day in cracks and crevices and under bark and debris.

WHAT THEY EAT: Earwigs in the family Forficulidae feed on dead and decaying plants and occasionally living plants, fungi, algae, moss, lichen, and small insects like aphids. Those in Labiduridae hunt and eat other arthropods, including caterpillars and spiders.

LIFE CYCLE: Nymphs and adults are found in the same habitat; females protect their eggs and young nymphs within burrows for a few weeks. Nymphs go through four to five molts before reaching adulthood, and earwigs overwinter as adults.

APPROX. NUMBER OF KNOWN SPECIES: 1,800 worldwide (27 in North America).

RELATIVE ABUNDANCE: Native species are not very abundant in the United States, where the most abundant, commonly seen earwig is the European earwig (*Forficula auricularia*), a species introduced from Europe around 1910 and which can be seen on flowers, garden vegetables, and more.

NOTES OF INTEREST:

- Native earwig species are not very abundant in the United States and the the most commonly seen earwig is the European earwig, introduced species that may be a pest in some fruit crop systems.
- When disturbed, earwigs respond by trying to wedge deeper into the soil, looking to get as much direct contact of their body with the substrate.
- Mothers become cannibalistic a few weeks in to providing care for their young.

FIGURE 122—Striped earwig (*Labidura riparia*).

FIGURE 123—Female European earwig (*Forficula auricularia*) guarding eggs.

- Some species have glands on their abdomen from which they emit stinky fluid to deter predators.
- Their common name is derived from meritless folklore about these insects entering people's ears.
- Earwigs do not bite but can pinch using their cerci.
- The European earwig can cause damage to plants at high population levels, particularly to seedlings and soft fruits (e.g., raspberries).

WEBSPINNERS • GRASSHOPPERS

28. WEBSPINNERS

PHYLUM: Arthropoda » **CLASS:** Insecta » **ORDER:** Embioptera, also known as Embiidina
SIZE: 0.08–0.87" (2–22 mm).
ECOLOGICAL ROLE: Webspinners may contribute to decomposition.
DESCRIPTION: Webspinners have beaded antennae and slender, elongated brown bodies. Their front legs are swollen in appearance and house silk glands used to make silken galleries. Males have wings but females do not.
WHERE THEY ARE FOUND: Webspinners live in silken galleries under grass roots, bark, or stones. Males can be seen near artificial lights at night. These insects are found only in warm regions, and they are less common or absent in the northern half of the United States.
WHAT THEY EAT: Adult and juvenile webspinners consume dead plant material as well as lichens and moss.
LIFE CYCLE: These insects live in maternal groups within their galleries, and females provide some care for their young. They have only one generation per year.
APPROX. NUMBER OF KNOWN SPECIES: 380 worldwide (11 in North America).
RELATIVE ABUNDANCE: These insects are uncommon.
NOTES OF INTEREST:

FIGURE 124—Male webspinner.

FIGURE 125—Native webspinner (Anisembia texana).

- Male webspinners often move backward within galleries to avoid friction with their wings, which they fold forward.

- Female webspinners do not disperse very far since they do not fly.

29. GRASSHOPPERS

PHYLUM: Arthropoda » **CLASS:** Insecta » **ORDER:** Orthoptera » **FAMILY:** Acrididae
SIZE: 0.2–4.5" (5–115 mm).
ECOLOGICAL ROLE: Grasshoppers are herbivores and lay their eggs in soil.
DESCRIPTION: Grasshoppers have antennae shorter than their body. They have powerful hind legs used for jumping. Their bodies are frequently brown or greyish, with patterns to help blend in with their surroundings; their hind wings, seen only when they take flight, may be brightly colored.
WHERE THEY ARE FOUND: Adults are found on vegetation, particularly herbaceous plants. They lay eggs in chambers in the soil 1" (2.54 cm) or more deep.
WHAT THEY EAT: Grasshoppers eat plants of all types, and some species can be very destructive of crops or rangeland; some may also scavenge for dead plant material.
LIFE CYCLE: Female grasshoppers drill into soil using their abdomen, secreting a substance that hardens to form a protective case around eggs laid within underground chambers. Nymphs resemble adults, except for their

FIGURE 126—Grasshopper laying eggs in soil.

underdeveloped wings. Most species overwinter as eggs, but a few do overwinter as nymphs or adults.

APPROX. NUMBER OF KNOWN SPECIES: 10,000 worldwide (620 in North America).

RELATIVE ABUNDANCE: Grasshoppers can be abundant periodically in some parts of the United States.

NOTES OF INTEREST:

- Grasshoppers will defend themselves by kicking or attempting to bite, or they will regurgitate their food onto predators.
- Parasites of grasshopper eggs include blister beetles and bee flies, the larvae of which feed on the eggs.
- Grasshoppers are an important food source for birds, reptiles, and mammals.
- During the day, they sing by rubbing their hind legs against their wings (unlike katydids that sing at night).

FIGURE 127—Carolina grasshopper (*Dissosteira carolina*).

30. MOLE CRICKETS AND CAMEL CRICKETS

PHYLUM: Arthropoda » **CLASS:** Insecta » **ORDER:** Orthoptera » **FAMILIES:** Gryllotalpidae, Rhaphidophoridae

SIZE: 0.2–1.97" (5–50 mm).

ECOLOGICAL ROLE: Mole crickets (Gryllotalpidae) move soil through their burrowing activities. Both mole crickets and camel crickets (Rhaphidophoridae) fit into food webs as herbivores, decomposers, and predators.

DESCRIPTION: Camel crickets are brown or dark in color, appear humpbacked, are wingless, and have long hind legs and long, sensitive antennae. Mole crickets have brown bodies, short antennae, and powerful, shovellike front legs.

WHERE THEY ARE FOUND: Camel crickets are found in dark, moist places such as in leaf litter and mammal burrows, and under logs or stones. Mole crickets are often within underground burrows searching for food. Both groups are more active at night.

WHAT THEY EAT: Camel crickets eat plant debris and small arthropods, while mole crickets eat soil insects, earthworms, and plant roots.

LIFE CYCLE: Mole crickets and camel crickets lay eggs in chambers in moist soil. Eggs hatch into nymphs, which resemble adults but are without wings through 10 molts. These crickets overwinter as nymphs or adults.

APPROX. NUMBER OF KNOWN SPECIES: 600 camel crickets worldwide (114 in the United States) and 50 mole crickets worldwide (seven in the United States).

FIGURE 128—Northern mole cricket (*Neocurtilla hexadactyla*).

FIGURE 129—Camel cricket (*Ceuthophilus* sp.).

RELATIVE ABUNDANCE: These are not generally abundant.

NOTES OF INTEREST:

- Camel crickets do not chirp, but mole crickets sing within their underground tunnels, rubbing their wings together. Male mole crickets will build a special tunnel for courtship, designed to amplify their chirps.
- Camel crickets are also called cave crickets or spider crickets.

- Mole cricket burrows are often 6–8" (150–200 mm) below the surface. Galleries longer than 20' (6.1 m) have been found. Sometimes they can cause minor damage to turf.

31. BURROWER BUGS

PHYLUM: Arthropoda » CLASS: Insecta » ORDER: Hemiptera » FAMILY: Cydnidae

SIZE: 0.12–0.39" (3–10 mm).

ECOLOGICAL ROLE: Burrower bugs, as their name suggests, are burrowers and may dig as deep as 17.7" (45 cm) into the ground; they are also herbivores in food webs.

DESCRIPTION: Burrower bugs are broadly oval, resembling small stink bugs in shape, and are black or brown. They have forelegs modified for digging, flattened with rows of stiff bristles, and their hind legs are also spiny.

WHERE THEY ARE FOUND: Burrower bugs burrow in upper soil layers, around roots, and under stones or wood. They are most often seen at night.

WHAT THEY EAT: Burrower bugs tap into plant roots to drink juices.

LIFE CYCLE: Female burrower bugs lay eggs in a chamber among roots and remain with their eggs until they hatch. Young then crawl onto their mother and drink her microbe-containing anal secretions during the first days of their life. Young pass through five instars before reaching maturity.

APPROX. NUMBER OF KNOWN SPECIES: 770 worldwide (43 in North America).

RELATIVE ABUNDANCE: Burrower bugs are not very abundant.

NOTES OF INTEREST:

- Only those that are nursed by their mothers survive to feed on plant roots; mothers pass on bacteria that produce much-needed vitamins.

FIGURE 130—White-margined burrower bug (*Sehirus cinctus*).

32. CICADAS

PHYLUM: Arthropoda » CLASS: Insecta » ORDER: Hemiptera » FAMILY: Cicadidae

SIZE: 0.98–1.97" (25–50 mm).

ECOLOGICAL ROLE: Cicadas influence soil systems as herbivores and burrowers.

DESCRIPTION: Cicadas have dark bodies with green markings, bulging eyes, short antennae, and membranous, transparent wings that they hold like a tent over themselves. Nymphs have well-developed digging legs, used for tunneling in the soil to reach tree roots. Adult periodical cicadas (*Magicicada*) have red eyes and orange wing veins.

WHERE THEY ARE FOUND: Cicadas live in grasslands and forests.

WHAT THEY EAT: Larvae consume sap from tree roots, and adults drink plant sap.

LIFE CYCLE: Female cicadas insert their eggs into twigs; when the eggs hatch, the nymphs fall to the ground, dig down to the tree's roots, and then tap the roots with their piercing, sucking mouthparts. Their development largely takes place

FIGURE 131—Adult periodical cicada (*Magicicada* sp.).

FIGURE 132—Adult dog-day cicada (*Neotibicen canicularis*).

underground. Nymphs emerge to molt into adults in spring or summer. Life span varies by species; cicadas that emerge annually in the summer—for example, dog-day cicadas (*Neotibicen canicularis*)— spend four to seven years underground before emerging, while periodical cicadas have 13- or 17-year emergence cycles.

APPROX. NUMBER OF KNOWN SPECIES: 1,500 worldwide (170 in North America).

RELATIVE ABUNDANCE: Cicadas can be very numerous, especially during emergence of periodical cicada broods. An estimate in Indiana found 20,000 larval burrows counted under one apple tree.

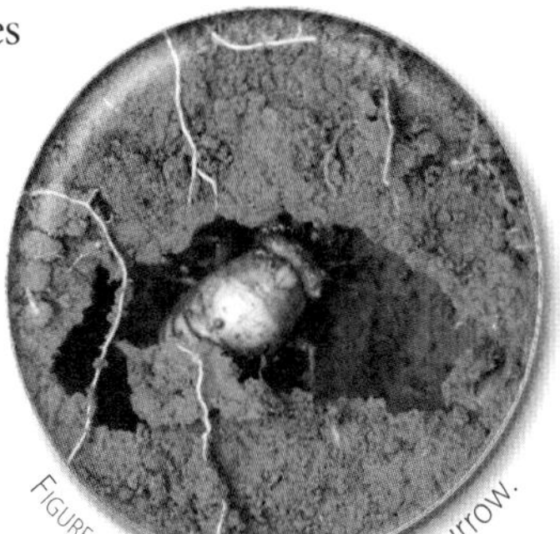

FIGURE 133—Cicada nymph in burrow.

NOTES OF INTEREST:

- Cicada parasites include beetle larvae from the family Rhipiceridae. Adult female rhipicerids lay their eggs on trees near cicada eggs, and their larvae then work their way through the soil to find the nymphal cicadas.
- Each cicada species has its own song.
- Searching for cicada shells, the split exoskeleton left behind when a nymph transforms into an adult, is a common pastime for kids in the summer.

33. APHIDS, PHYLLOXERANS, SCALES, AND MEALYBUGS

PHYLUM: Arthropoda » **CLASS:** Insecta » **ORDER:** Hemiptera » **SUPERFAMILY:** Coccoidea » **FAMILIES:** Aphididae, Coccidae, Diaspididae, Margarodidae, Phylloxeridae, Pseudococcidae

SIZE: 0.039–0.31" (1–8 mm).

ECOLOGICAL ROLE: In soil food webs, these insects are fungivores and herbivores, and some can be economically damaging crop pests.

DESCRIPTION: Aphid, phylloxeran, scale, and mealybug adults can be winged or wingless, can secrete waxy fibers or powder to cover their bodies and have beaks for sucking plant juices. Aphids and phylloxerans have soft, globular or pear-shaped bodies. Aphids have long antennae, and they have tubelike structures, called cornicles, at the end of the abdomen. Phylloxerans hold their wings flat over their body at rest. Scales belong to the families Coccidae, Diaspididae, and Margarodidae. They have armorlike, flattened, domed coverings that blend in easily on plant parts. Mealybugs are in the family Pseudococcidae and are often light in color, with a cottony appearance. Scale and mealybug nymphs have legs and are mobile, but in most species, the adult females usually lack wings, legs, and antennae; they settle into one spot to feed throughout their life. Once they settle, scales and mealybugs secrete a waxy covering over their body.

FIGURE 134—Mealybugs.

CICADAS • APHIDS, PHYLLOXERANS, SCALES, AND MEALYBUGS

APHIDS, PHYLLOXERANS, SCALES, AND MEALYBUGS

Figure 135—Sugarbeet root aphid infestation.

Figure 136—Aphid on root.

Figure 137—Ground mealybug infestation and nymph.

Figure 138—Female phylloxeran nymph.

Figure 139—Female phylloxeran adult.

WHERE THEY ARE FOUND: These insects live within leaf litter and in the soil among roots; many aphids, scales, and mealybugs are also found aboveground on stems and leaves.

WHAT THEY EAT: Soil-dwelling aphids, phylloxerans, scales, and mealybugs feed on fungal hyphae and plant sap from roots. Phylloxerans often have a single plant species as a host, and some form galls on those plants. Scales and mealybugs feed on plant sap.

LIFE CYCLE: Aphids and phylloxerans can have complex life cycles, with changing body forms (e.g., winged vs. wingless) and reproductive strategies (e.g., parthenogenetic as opposed to sexual) between generations. Most aphid and phylloxeran species overwinter as eggs and can have many generations during the growing season. Aphids can also give birth to living young. Female scales and mealybugs give birth to living young, and some give birth without mating.

APPROX. NUMBER OF KNOWN SPECIES: 3,500 aphids worldwide (1,300 in North America), 75 phylloxerans worldwide, and 6,000 scales and mealybugs worldwide (1,100 in North America). Note: these estimates include both aboveground and belowground species.

RELATIVE ABUNDANCE: Aphids can be very abundant, increasing their populations quickly if conditions are favorable.

NOTES OF INTEREST:

- Some ants tend aphid colonies, guarding them from predators in exchange for honeydew (excessive sap that is secreted by aphids), and will carry root aphids to newly sprouted roots.
- Aphids are serious pests of many cultivated plants and transmit a number of plant diseases. Mealybugs and scales can also be problematic pests of crops and ornamental plants.

- Phylloxerans are named for the effects they have on plants (*phyllo* = leaf; *xero* = dry).
- Aphid cornicles secrete defensive fluids.
- As new nymphs, mealybugs and scales roam to find a spot in which to settle. Female scales will remain to feed in one spot for the rest of their lives, and although mealybugs are slightly more mobile as adults, they don't move far from their feeding spot.

34. SCORPIONFLIES AND HANGINGFLIES

PHYLUM: Arthropoda » **CLASS:** Insecta » **ORDER:** Mecoptera » **FAMILIES:** Bittacidae, Panorpidae
SIZE: 0.35–0.87" (9–22 mm).

ECOLOGICAL ROLE: In soil food webs, scorpionflies and hangingflies are predators and decomposers.

DESCRIPTION: Adults have slender bodies, threadlike antennae, and an elongated face that looks a bit horselike. Scorpionflies (Panorpidae) have chewing mouthparts and males have a bulbous abdominal segment that is often curved above the back, much like a scorpion. Hangingflies (Bittacidae) have long, slender legs with spines and biting jaws. Larvae are caterpillar-like, and scorpionfly larvae have bumps and hairs that hold pieces of dirt or leaves that help keep them camouflaged from predators.

WHERE THEY ARE FOUND: Scorpionfly and hangingfly eggs, larvae, and pupae are found in the soil and leaf litter. Adult scorpionflies are also found on litter and occasionally on flowers. Hangingfly adults hang from leaves by their legs to catch prey that comes near.

WHAT THEY EAT: Scorpionfly larvae and adults scavenge for dead insects, snails, or worms on the soil surface or in leaf litter. Hangingfly adults eat caterpillars, flies, moths, and aphids.

LIFE CYCLE: Scorpionflies and hangingflies lay eggs in the soil, and larvae live in tunnels they create until pupation.

APPROX. NUMBER OF KNOWN SPECIES: 170 hangingflies worldwide (10 in North America); 360 scorpionflies worldwide (55 in North America).

RELATIVE ABUNDANCE: Data unavailable.

NOTES OF INTEREST:

- Snow scorpionflies (in the family Boreidae) are wingless and live gregariously in communities. Snow scorpionflies are most active in winter and early spring, and they can be seen walking across snow. Snow scorpionflies feed on liverworts and mosses and are less common on agricultural lands than hangingflies or scorpionflies.
- Adult scorpionflies sometimes steal food from spider webs.
- This group of insects are not true flies, despite their common names; they may be most closely related to fleas.

FIGURE 140—Scorpionfly (*Panorpa* sp.) adult.

FIGURE 141—Hangingfly larva.

FIGURE 142—Hangingfly (*Bittacus* sp.) adult.

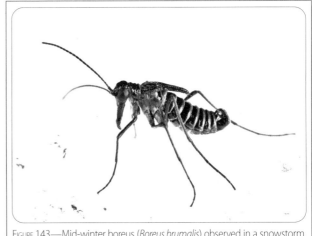

FIGURE 143—Mid-winter boreus (*Boreus brumalis*) observed in a snowstorm.

35. ANTLIONS

PHYLUM: Arthropoda » **CLASS:** Insecta » **ORDER:** Neuroptera » **FAMILY:** Myrmeleontidae

SIZE: Larvae are 0.39–0.87" (10–22 mm) and adults are 1.57–3.15" (40–80 mm).

ECOLOGICAL ROLE: Antlion larvae are voracious predators and burrowers.

DESCRIPTION: Adult antlions resemble damselflies, with long, clubbed antennae. Larvae have a round body, with a flat head and powerful sicklelike jaws.

WHERE THEY ARE FOUND: Larvae are found at the bottom of small, conical pits in the soil where they hide and wait for insect prey to fall in. Adults fly at night.

WHAT THEY EAT: Larvae eat ants and other arthropods that live or travel on the soil surface. Adults may be predaceous or consume pollen and nectar.

LIFE CYCLE: Antlions lay eggs in the soil. Larvae reside in the soil, catching prey, and can survive long periods without food (it can take several years to reach adulthood when food is not plentiful). Cocoons are made of sand, soil, or other materials, along with spun silk, and are buried in the soil.

APPROX. NUMBER OF KNOWN SPECIES: 2,000 worldwide (90 in North America).

RELATIVE ABUNDANCE: Antlions are less common in northern areas; they are most abundant in dry, sandy habitats.

NOTES OF INTEREST:

- Antlion larvae will throw soil at prey if needed so that they fall down the pit into their jaws.
- Larvae are known as doodlebugs, so named for the trails they leave behind them on the soil.
- Antlions can feel the vibrations from prey in their pit, detecting movement with the sensory bristles all over their body.
- Larvae seize prey with their pincers, immobilizing them with a secretion and then sucking out their insides after digestive fluids have done their work.
- Some larvae may move throughout the day according to their solar exposure or may bury themselves deeper when it gets too hot.
- Adults are feeble fliers.

FIGURE 144—Common antlion (*Brachynemurus* sp.).

FIGURE 145—Spotted-winged antlion (*Dendroleon* sp.) laying eggs in soil.

FIGURE 146—Antlion larva.

FIGURE 147—Antlion larval pit traps, close-up of larva hiding in a trap.

36. SOIL-DWELLING MOTH CATERPILLARS

PHYLUM: Arthropoda » **CLASS:** Insecta » **ORDER:** Lepidoptera » **FAMILIES:** Hepialidae, Noctuidae, Psychidae, Tineidae
SIZE: 0.24–1.97" (6–50 mm).

ECOLOGICAL ROLE: Only a few groups of moths have species with caterpillars that live in the soil. Caterpillars of these soil-dwelling moths are herbivores, decomposers, fungivores, and predators in soil food webs.

DESCRIPTION: These caterpillars are soft bodied, with a hardened head and dark body coloration. Bagworm (Psychidae) caterpillars build silken cases with sand, small stones, or pieces of plants. Adult bagworm moth males have wings, while females are wingless and remain in their larval case. Adults of other soil moths—including ghost moths (Hepialidae), cutworms (Noctuidae), and clothes moths (Tineidae)—are often drab in color, with camouflage patterns on their wings.

WHERE THEY ARE FOUND: Ghost moth and cutworm caterpillars are found in the roots of plants. Bagworm caterpillars are found in soil tunnels inside cases of spun silk and debris, some within ant colonies. Clothes moth caterpillars are found inside a tubular web in the ground, as deep as 1.97' (0.6 m).

WHAT THEY EAT: Caterpillars of these moths eat roots, decaying plants and wood, algae, moss, lichen, and fungi.

LIFE CYCLE: Caterpillars, the larval stage of moths, feed in the soil or leaf litter and pupate in the soil. Adults live aboveground.

APPROX. NUMBER OF KNOWN SPECIES: 3,000 clothes moths worldwide (190 in North America), 20,000 cutworms worldwide (2,500 in North America), 1,100 bagworms worldwide (28 in North America), and 500 ghost moths worldwide (20 in North America) Note: not all members of these families dwell in the soil as caterpillars.

RELATIVE ABUNDANCE: Population densities of psychid moths can be high.

NOTES OF INTEREST:

- Some cutworm caterpillars live within roots and pupate in tunnels in the soil lined with silk. There are also a few root-boring caterpillars in the families Sesiidae and Pyralidae.
- Some noctuid caterpillars hide in the soil during the day and feed above ground at night or drag plants into their tunnels.

FIGURE 148—Bagworm moth (*Thyridopteryx* sp.) caterpillar and the protective bag of debris it built.

FIGURE 149—Granulate cutworm (*Feltia subterranea*) caterpillar. Larvae hide under plants or in the soil during the day and emerge to feed on leaves and stems at night.

FIGURE 150—Adult imperial moth (*Eacles imperialis*). This is one of the moth species that pupates underground.

FLIES (DIPTERA) are the only group of winged insects that have just one pair of wings. Adults usually have sponging or tubular mouthparts but never chewing mouthparts. Fly larvae are legless. Many flies are soil insects for one or more stages in their life cycle; at least 75 out of the 108 families of flies found in North America are part of soil systems. Fly larvae make considerable contributions to soil communities as decomposers of plant material or carrion and as predators or parasites; a number of flies pupate in the soil.

NONBITING MIDGES

37. NONBITING MIDGES

PHYLUM: Arthropoda » **CLASS:** Insecta » **ORDER:** Diptera » **FAMILY:** Chironomidae

SIZE: 0.059–1.18" (1.5 mm–3 cm).

ECOLOGICAL ROLE: These larval flies are decomposers, helping to recycle plant debris.

DESCRIPTION: Larvae are legless but have two fleshy prolegs behind the head. Many adults are small and resemble mosquitoes without biting mouthparts, and their wings have no scales. Adult males have feathery antennae.

WHERE THEY ARE FOUND: Larvae of soil-dwelling species occur in decaying matter and soil, or under bark (many in this family are aquatic). Adults swarm in clouds near their larval habitat.

WHAT THEY EAT: Larvae eat detritus, algae, and fungi; a few are predators or parasites. Adults either do not feed or consume pollen, nectar, or honeydew.

LIFE CYCLE: Nonbiting midges lay eggs in soil. The time from egg through larvae and pupae to adult ranges from a week to a year or more, depending on the species. Adults are short-lived.

APPROX. NUMBER OF KNOWN SPECIES: 7,000 worldwide (2,000 in North America).

RELATIVE ABUNDANCE: Larvae can be very abundant—as high as 10,000 per square meter—and are important food sources for fish and other animals.

NOTES OF INTEREST:

- The larvae of aquatic nonbiting midges are indicators of water quality; some species are found only in unpolluted waters, while others can live in polluted streams.
- Nonbiting midge larvae wiggle through soil using their two prolegs and spines for traction.

FIGURE 151—Male midge adult with characteristic plumose antennae.

FIGURE 152—Nonbiting midge larvae.

FIGURE 153—*Stenochironomus poecilopterus* adult female.

. . . .

38. MARCH FLIES

PHYLUM: Arthropoda » **CLASS:** Insecta » **ORDER:** Diptera » **FAMILY:** Bibionidae

SIZE: 0.24–0.98" (6 mm–2.5 cm).

ECOLOGICAL ROLE: These decomposers help make humus by consuming fallen leaves.

DESCRIPTION: Adults have dark bodies, some with a red or yellow thorax, and lots of short bristles all over their bodies. Larvae are blackish-brown, have rows of fleshy projections covering their bodies, and have chewing mouthparts.

FIGURE 154—March fly (*Bibio* spp.) male [left] and female [right] adults.

FIGURE 155—March fly (Bibionidae) larvae.

WHERE THEY ARE FOUND: Larvae live in decaying organic matter like leaf litter or dung, or they live among plant roots. Adults tend to fly in spring or summer and can be seen on flowers.

WHAT THEY EAT: Larvae feed preferably on decaying leaves, and they also consume fungi, algae, detritus, or plant roots. Adults may drink nectar.

LIFE CYCLE: Adults emerge in masses and are short-lived. Females fly into swarms of males to find a mate, and paired flies stay attached to their mates for a day or more. Females dig a small chamber in the soil to lay their eggs.

APPROX. NUMBER OF KNOWN SPECIES: 1,100 worldwide (60 in North America).

RELATIVE ABUNDANCE: These flies can be very abundant, with 3,000 to 12,000 larvae per square meter.

NOTES OF INTEREST:

- Lovebugs (*Plecia nearctica*) are abundant in the southern United States. In Florida, mass emergence of adults can be a nuisance for drivers.

39. CRANE FLIES

PHYLUM: Arthropoda » **CLASS:** Insecta »
  ORDER: Diptera » **FAMILY:** Tipulidae

SIZE: 0.12–2.36" (3 mm–6 cm).

ECOLOGICAL ROLE: Crane fly larvae make notable contributions to the decomposition of leaf litter, particularly in woodlands.

DESCRIPTION: Crane fly larvae are cylindrical and soft bodied with fleshy projections on their posterior; they have rasping jaws, and their head can be retracted into their thorax. Adults have very long, spindly legs and long beaks, and they are often mistaken for large mosquitoes.

FIGURE 156—Crane fly (*Tipula* sp.) adult.

WHERE THEY ARE FOUND: Crane fly larvae are found in moist soils or leaf litter, particularly in forests but also along the shores of ponds and rivers, in moss or fungi, and under bark or in decaying wood. Adults may be seen on flowers but may be most visible near lights at night.

WHAT THEY EAT: Larvae eat detritus, algae, and fungi, and some feed underground on plant roots or eat other insects. Adults of some species drink nectar or sap, but many don't feed as adults.

FIGURE 157—Crane fly larva.

CRANE FLIES

• SOLDIER FLIES

LIFE CYCLE: Crane flies lay eggs in the soil and overwinter as larvae. Adults emerge after pupation and fly for several weeks. Crane flies usually have one generation a year.

APPROX. NUMBER OF KNOWN SPECIES: 15,000 worldwide (1,500 in North America).

RELATIVE ABUNDANCE: Larvae of these flies can be very abundant.

NOTES OF INTEREST:

- Chionea crane flies do not have wings (but still have their halteres, knobbed appendages unique to flies, located in place of hindwings that help flies to rotate and balance) and can be seen walking on the snow on warm winter days.
- Contrary to urban legend, crane flies are neither giant mosquitoes nor do they eat mosquitoes—the few adult crane flies that feed have fly mouthparts suited only for occasional nectar.

FIGURE 158—Crane fly (*Tipula* sp.) adult female laying eggs in soil.

40. SOLDIER FLIES

PHYLUM: Arthropoda » **CLASS:** Insecta » **ORDER:** Diptera » **FAMILY:** Stratiomyidae
SIZE: 0.2–1.4" (5–35 mm).

ECOLOGICAL ROLE: In soil food webs, these flies are primarily decomposers as larvae. Adults may contribute to plant pollination.

DESCRIPTION: Larvae have segmented bodies that are rough and leathery, helping them survive droughts in the summer. Adults are often colorful, and some mimic wasps and bees. Some have a broad, flattened abdomen and fold their wings flat over their backs.

WHERE THEY ARE FOUND: Larvae prefer soil with decaying plant matter. Adults are often found on flowers.

WHAT THEY EAT: Larvae eat detritus, soil algae, fungi, and dung, and a few (in the subfamily Pachygastrinae) are predators of bark beetle (Scolytidae) larvae. Adults drink nectar.

LIFE CYCLE: Soldier flies deposit eggs near the larval food source (e.g., manure), and the larvae pass through several molts before pupation.

APPROX. NUMBER OF KNOWN SPECIES: 2,000 worldwide (250 in North America).

RELATIVE ABUNDANCE: Data unavailable.

NOTES OF INTEREST:

- Soldier fly larval skin contains calcium carbonate.
- The larvae of black soldier flies (*Hermetia illucens*) are a food source for many animals, and researchers are exploring them as a possible protein source for humans and livestock.

FIGURE 159—Black soldier fly (*Hermetia illucens*) adult.

FIGURE 160—Black soldier fly (*Hermetia illucens*) larvae.

41. SNIPE FLIES

PHYLUM: Arthropoda » CLASS: Insecta » ORDER: Diptera » FAMILY: Rhagionidae

SIZE: 0.24–0.59" (6 mm–1.5 cm).

ECOLOGICAL ROLE: Snipe flies are predators in soil food webs.

DESCRIPTION: Adults have rounded heads, large eyes, and a long, tapering abdomen. Many have dark spots or patterns on their wings.

FIGURE 161—Snipe fly larva.

FIGURE 162—Golden-backed snipe fly (*Chrysopilus thoracicus*) adult male.

WHERE THEY ARE FOUND: Larvae are found in leaf litter. Adults occur nearby, usually on foliage.

WHAT THEY EAT: Adults and larvae are predaceous on small insects. Adults perch on vegetation to catch their prey. Larvae strike at other soil insects from the leaf litter.

LIFE CYCLE: Snipe flies lay eggs in leaf litter. Larvae likely overwinter in the leaf litter and there is likely one generation per year. Adults emerge in late spring and early summer.

APPROX. NUMBER OF KNOWN SPECIES: 400 worldwide (100 in North America).

RELATIVE ABUNDANCE: Data unavailable.

NOTES OF INTEREST:

- Few snipe fly species bite people, but Rocky Mountain bite flies (*Symphoromyia*) do suck blood and can inflict bites on people across their range in the western United States.

42. MOTH FLIES

PHYLUM: Arthropoda » CLASS: Insecta » ORDER: Diptera » FAMILY: Psychodidae

SIZE: 0.12–0.24" (3–6 mm).

ECOLOGICAL ROLE: Moth flies contribute to the decomposition of plant matter and fungi.

DESCRIPTION: Adults are hairy and mothlike, with long antennae, and they hold their wings like a roof over their body. Larvae are eyeless and legless, with hairs or bristles on their body. They can add chunks of soil to cover their backs, perhaps as camouflage.

FIGURE 163—Moth fly larva.

WHERE THEY ARE FOUND: Larvae are found in very moist woodland soil, decaying leaves, rotting logs, and moss, and several species are in streams. Adults occur in moist places, including drains in buildings and near sewers.

WHAT THEY EAT: Larvae and adults consume plant detritus, fungi, or algae.

LIFE CYCLE: Moth flies lay eggs in water films or wet soils. Development time from egg to adult can be as short as eight days or up to one month.

APPROX. NUMBER OF KNOWN SPECIES: 450 worldwide (115 in North America).

RELATIVE ABUNDANCE: Data unavailable.

NOTES OF INTEREST:

- Phlebotomine sand flies (Phlebotominae) suck blood and are found in the southern United States and tropics. They can transfer leishmaniasis, a disease caused by a protozoan parasite.
- Moth flies can sometimes be considered a nuisance if they breed in bathroom drains in buildings.

FIGURE 164—Moth fly (*Psychoda* sp.) adult.

43. SIGNAL FLIES

PHYLUM: Arthropoda » **CLASS:** Insecta » **ORDER:** Diptera » **FAMILY:** Platystomatidae
SIZE: 0.12–0.47" (3–12 mm).
ECOLOGICAL ROLE: Signal flies are herbivores or decomposers in soil food webs.
DESCRIPTION: Adults have brown or black wing markings and shiny, metallic bodies. Larvae are soft-bodied, cream in color, and have a small, hardened head.
WHERE THEY ARE FOUND: Signal fly larvae occur in decaying vegetation. Adults are found on foliage or tree trunks.
WHAT THEY EAT: Some larvae eat root nodules, which contain nutrients as well as bacteria. Others are found on carrion and decaying vegetation. Adults may visit flowers, decaying fruit, or decomposing organic matter.
LIFE CYCLE: Signal flies deposit eggs near a larval food source. After they hatch, larvae must find the intended food nearby. Those that feed on root nodules, for example, must travel through the soil under plants to find nodules on which to feed. These flies likely overwinter as larvae, and there is likely only one generation of these flies each year.

FIGURE 165—Signal fly adult on decomposing matter.

APPROX. NUMBER OF KNOWN SPECIES: 1,100 worldwide (41 in North America).
RELATIVE ABUNDANCE: Data unavailable.
NOTES OF INTEREST:

- These flies are commonly called signal flies because their wings are in almost constant motion, flicking back and forth as though the flies are giving signals.
- Signal flies are among the few animals that utilize root nodules as a food source.

44. BLOW FLIES, FLESH FLIES, AND HOUSE FLIES

PHYLUM: Arthropoda » **CLASS:** Insecta » **ORDER:** Diptera » **FAMILIES:** Calliphoridae, Muscidae, Sarcophagidae
SIZE: 0.08–0.87" (2–22 mm) but usually 0.24–0.55" (6–14 mm).
ECOLOGICAL ROLE: Blow flies (Calliphoridae), flesh flies (Sarcophagidae), and house flies (Muscidae) can be decomposers of plant and animal matter in soil food webs, as well as predators or parasites. Some of these flies are of economic importance, causing harm to domestic animals or humans.
DESCRIPTION: Blow flies are green or blue metallic in color. Flesh flies are dark with gray stripes on their thorax. House flies are typically gray, brown, yellow, or black in color.
WHERE THEY ARE FOUND: These flies are common near decaying materials, including dung, feces, and carrion. Some can be found parasitizing vertebrates.
WHAT THEY EAT: Larvae eat dung, carrion, decaying vegetation, and living tissue of animals (e.g., feeding on flesh in an open wound on a horse); some are predators of other arthropods, earthworms, and snails; and a few

FIGURE 166—The common green bottle fly (*Lucilia sericata*, adult [left] and larva/pupa [right]) is one of the most common blowflies species.

FIGURE 167—House fly (*Musca domestica*, adults [left] and immature life stages [right]) are common both in- and out-side homes.

FIGURE 168—In addition to feeding on animal matter, flesh flies will feed on decaying vegetable matter.

are parasitoids of other insects. Adults feed on nectar, sap, honeydew, fruit juices, or fluids from animal bodies or waste.

LIFE CYCLE: These insects lay eggs near a preferred food source, in either decaying matter or in living tissue. Life cycles can be completed in as little as a week.

APPROX. NUMBER OF KNOWN SPECIES: 1,500 blow flies worldwide (84 in North America), 3,100 flesh flies worldwide (400 in North America), and 5,200 house flies worldwide (700 in North America).

RELATIVE ABUNDANCE: These flies can be very common, especially near stables and on hog, poultry, or cattle farms.

NOTES OF INTEREST:

- Some species of house flies (e.g., *Musca domestica*) are vectors of pathogens harmful to humans (e.g., typhoid fever and dysentery). The horn fly (*Haematobia irritans*), also in the family Muscidae, breeds in cow dung and is a serious pest of cattle.
- The screwworm fly (*Cochliomyia hominivorax*), in the family Calliphoridae, lays its eggs in open sores or inside nostrils of its host.

- One group of flesh flies, species in the Sarcophagidae subfamily Miltogramminae, are cleptoparasites and develop in the nests of predatory wasps by feeding on the arthropods intended as food provisions for wasp young. Other flesh flies frequent pitcher plants, feeding on the insects drowned in the pitcher's liquid.

FIGURE 169—Flesh fly (*Sarcophaga* sp.) larva.

BLOW FLIES, FLESH FLIES, AND HOUSE FLIES

45. DANCE FLIES

PHYLUM: Arthropoda » **CLASS:** Insecta » **ORDER:** Diptera » **FAMILY:** Empididae

SIZE: 0.06–0.47" (1.5–12 mm).

ECOLOGICAL ROLE: Dance flies are decomposers and predators.

DESCRIPTION: Adults are dark in color with long, spiny legs.

WHERE THEY ARE FOUND: Dance fly larvae live in soil, decaying vegetation, and under bark, and some are in dung or fungus. Adults swarm, flying up and down near larval habitat, and can also be found on flowers.

WHAT THEY EAT: Adults prey on a variety of other insects, including black flies (Simuliidae) and mosquitoes

FIGURE 170—Dance fly (*Rhamphomyia* sp.) adult.

(Culicidae), and some drink nectar. Larvae eat decaying matter, and some are predators of other soil insects.

LIFE CYCLE: Females enter swarms of males to choose a mate. They lay eggs in soil or in decaying vegetation.

APPROX. NUMBER OF KNOWN SPECIES: 4,000 worldwide (725 in North America).

RELATIVE ABUNDANCE: Data unavailable.

NOTES OF INTEREST:

- Male dance flies provide nuptial gifts to attract females.
- This group of flies isn't well studied, so there is much to learn about their natural history.

FIGURE 171—Female dance fly feeding on nuptial gift.

46. LONG-LEGGED FLIES

PHYLUM: Arthropoda » **CLASS:** Insecta » **ORDER:** Diptera » **FAMILY:** Dolichopodidae

SIZE: Less than 0.04–0.35" (1–9 mm).

ECOLOGICAL ROLE: Long-legged flies are predators in soil systems and above ground.

DESCRIPTION: Adults are small, with metallic green-blue-copper bodies and long legs.

WHERE THEY ARE FOUND: Adults visit flowers. Larvae are found in decaying wood, leaf litter, and moist soil, and some live in water.

WHAT THEY EAT: Adults prey on small insects. Larvae are predaceous on soft-bodied prey like springtails or scales, but their diets are not fully known.

LIFE CYCLE: Long-legged flies lay eggs in soil. Pupation occurs in the soil within cocoons of soil particles.

APPROX. NUMBER OF KNOWN SPECIES: 7,400 worldwide (1,300 in North America).

RELATIVE ABUNDANCE: These are very abundant flies, particularly in forests and meadows, and near streams.

NOTES OF INTEREST:

- Adult long-legged flies have elaborate mating dances.
- This group of flies isn't well studied, and there is much to learn about their natural history.

FIGURE 172—Long-legged fly adult.

FIGURE 173—Female long-legged fly laying eggs in soil.

DANCE FLIES • LONG-LEGGED FLIES

47. ROBBER FLIES

PHYLUM: Arthropoda » **CLASS:** Insecta » **ORDER:** Diptera » **FAMILY:** Asilidae
SIZE: 0.3–1.4" (8 mm–3.5 cm).
ECOLOGICAL ROLE: Robber fly larvae are predators of other soil arthropods. In aboveground ecosystems, adults are predators of a wide range of insects.
DESCRIPTION: Larvae have soft bodies that are long and tapered at both ends. They are white to transparent in color, have a hardened head, and may grow as long as 1" (2.54 cm). Adults have large eyes with a depression between them, short antennae, and long, sturdy legs with bristles used for capturing prey. Some species mimic bees to a striking degree.
WHERE THEY ARE FOUND: Robber fly larvae live in the soil and litter, under bark, or in decayed logs. Adults are found on vegetation, where they are on the lookout for prey.
WHAT THEY EAT: Larvae consume insects in the soil, including beetle larvae (grubs) and grasshopper eggs. Adults capture other insects while in flight and are not selective—butterflies, bees, wasps, beetles, grasshoppers, flies, and many more.
LIFE CYCLE: Robber flies usually deposit eggs in the soil, but some species lay eggs on decaying wood. They overwinter as larvae, and pupation occurs in the soil. Development can take up to three years.
APPROX. NUMBER OF KNOWN SPECIES: 5,000 worldwide (1,000 in North America).
RELATIVE ABUNDANCE: Data unavailable.
NOTES OF INTEREST:

- Adults can catch prey on the wing, including skilled fliers like bees, dragonflies, and more.
- Robber fly larvae have no legs but are still fast predators.

Figure 174—Robber fly larva.

Figure 175—Robber fly with cricket prey.

Figure 176—Adult robber fly emerging from pupa underground.

48. BEE FLIES

PHYLUM: Arthropoda » **CLASS:** Insecta » **ORDER:** Diptera » **FAMILY:** Bombyliidae
SIZE: 0.35–0.98" (9 mm–2.5 cm).
ECOLOGICAL ROLE: Bee flies are parasitoids of soil insects as larvae and can be pollinators of some wild plants as adults.
DESCRIPTION: Adults have fuzzy, stout bodies and are shaped like bees. They have a long, thin proboscis used for sipping nectar. Larvae have robust, soft bodies that are legless and tapered at both ends.
WHERE THEY ARE FOUND: Adults are found visiting flowers, hovering while they retrieve nectar. Larvae are found on their hosts in the soil.
WHAT THEY EAT: Larvae are parasitoids of insects in the soil, including grasshopper eggs; wasp, bee, beetle, and antlion larvae; moth caterpillars; and other fly larvae. Adults drink nectar.

Figure 177—Bee fly larva.

BEE FLIES · FLOWER FLIES

FIGURE 178—Bee fly (*Bombylius* sp.) adult nectaring on a flower.

FIGURE 179—Greater bee fly (*Bombylius major*) adult.

LIFE CYCLE: Female bee flies deposit eggs in crevices in the ground near grasshopper eggs or other hosts, and the larvae must dig to find their host. The developing adult fly within its pupal case drills back out of the soil.

APPROX. NUMBER OF KNOWN SPECIES: 3,000 worldwide (800 in North America).

RELATIVE ABUNDANCE: Data unavailable.

NOTES OF INTEREST:

- Bee flies are some of the earliest pollinators to emerge in the spring and visit early-blooming plant species for nectar.

- Once larvae have found their host, they attach themselves with their mouthparts and suck out the body contents.

49. FLOWER FLIES

PHYLUM: Arthropoda » **CLASS:** Insecta » **ORDER:** Diptera » **FAMILY:** Syrphidae

SIZE: 0.3–0.78" (8–20 mm).

ECOLOGICAL ROLE: In the soil, larvae of some flower fly species are detritivores, helping to break down plant material or fungi, while other flower fly larvae are predatory, hunting small insects and arthropods. Adult flower flies are pollinators and are among the most effective group of non-bee pollinators of cultivated crops.

DESCRIPTION: Flower fly larvae are brown-gray-green, some with distinctive markings, stripes, or spines. Larvae are legless and swing their heads from side to side while hunting prey in leaf litter or on foliage. Adult flower flies have two wings; short, stout antennae; and large, broad eyes. Adults often have bright coloration, and many species mimic the coloration of bees or wasps, some to a striking degree.

WHERE THEY ARE FOUND: Flower fly larvae are found in ant mounds, leaf litter, and rotting wood, or on plants. Adults can be found in habitats with abundant flowering plants. Flower flies are less common in arid areas.

WHAT THEY EAT: Larvae in the soil consume decaying vegetation or wet wood. Predatory larvae in the soil hunt soil insects, especially social insects like ants and termites. Adults visit flowers, where they drink nectar and occasionally eat pollen.

FIGURE 180—Transverse-banded flower fly (*Eristalis transversa*) adult.

FIGURE 181—Predatory flower fly larva eating an aphid.

FIGURE 182—*Eristalis* spp. adults are important pollinators.

LIFE CYCLE: Flower flies lay eggs singly or in small clumps on foliage near larval food sources. Flower flies overwinter in leaf litter or soil as larvae, pupae, or adults. There can be one or multiple generations in a year (it varies with species).

APPROX. NUMBER OF KNOWN SPECIES: 6,000 worldwide (900 in North America).

RELATIVE ABUNDANCE: Many species can be abundant.

NOTES OF INTEREST:

- Adults hover at flowers, earning another common name, hover flies.
- Many aboveground species are important predators of crop pests like aphids and scales.
- Ant predators use chemical mimicry to avoid detection within ant nests; they produce a substance on their exoskeleton that is very similar to a substance produced by ants.
- Conservation strategies include protecting permanent habitat such as grasslands, meadows, field borders, and hedgerows. Since flower flies are less active under windy conditions, windbreaks may provide shelter and increase populations. Limit tilling, which may destroy overwintering sites.
- Some species are associated with fens, wetlands, bogs, and swamps, where the larvae feed on rotting wood or vegetation.
- Flower fly larvae have diverse feeding styles, and some are important filter feeders in water (e.g., *Eristalis* spp.).

FIGURE 183—Many flower fly species overwinter as larvae or pupae in leaf litter or underground.

FIGURE 184—*Eristalis* spp. larvae have long "tails" (spiracles) to breathe underwater or in mud.

FLOWER FLIES

BEETLES (COLEOPTERA) are insects with hardened forewings that cover their bodies. There are more than 370,000 species of beetles, making them one of the most diverse groups of organisms on the planet. Beetles contribute significantly to soil health through their roles as decomposers of plant material, carrion, dung, and fungi, as predators of other soil animals, and as burrowers in the soil.

FIREFLIES

50. FIREFLIES

PHYLUM: Arthropoda » CLASS: Insecta » ORDER: Coleoptera » FAMILY: Lampyridae
SIZE: 0.2–0.78" (5–20 mm).
ECOLOGICAL ROLE: Fireflies are predators in soil systems.
DESCRIPTION: Adults have soft, leathery wing covers—typically black with red or pale-brown markings—and have light-producing segments near the end of their abdomen. Female fireflies have shorter wings and fewer luminous segments than males, and many species are wingless. The predatory larvae have dark, elongated bodies and strong, sicklelike jaws.

WHERE THEY ARE FOUND: Larvae reside under bark and in damp areas where prey is found. Tall grasses in field edges or yards can shelter adults, which can also be found on flowers with open floral structures.

WHAT THEY EAT: Firefly larvae hunt snails, slugs, earthworms, caterpillars, and other soft-bodied insects in leaf litter and soil. Some adults are predatory or feed on nectar and pollen.

LIFE CYCLE: Fireflies may lay eggs singly or in clusters, just under soil or among grass roots. There are one to two generations a year, and larvae overwinter under bark or by burrowing into the soil. Fireflies pupate in soil, under rocks, or in leaf litter.

APPROX. NUMBER OF KNOWN SPECIES: 2,200 worldwide (170 in the United States).

RELATIVE ABUNDANCE: Fireflies are becoming increasingly rare as soils are more developed and disturbed.

NOTES OF INTEREST:
- Larvae are referred to by some as glow-worms because they are also luminescent; eggs of some species also glow. Their glowing warns predators that they are not tasty to eat.
- Using their luminescent organs to flash, fireflies attract mates in courtship rituals. Different species have distinct flashing patterns, to avoid confusion.
- Females of some species mimic the flash pattern of other firefly species to lure males, which they then eat.
- Firefly larvae are good hunters, searching soil burrows or tracking slug or snail trails to find their prey.

FIGURE 185—Firefly adult in flight.

FIGURE 186—Firefly adult.

FIGURE 187—Firefly pupa glowing.

FIGURE 188—Firefly larva.

51. SOLDIER BEETLES

PHYLUM: Arthropoda » **CLASS:** Insecta » **ORDER:** Coleoptera » **FAMILY:** Cantharidae

SIZE: 0.04–0.7" (1–18 mm).

ECOLOGICAL ROLE: Soldier beetle larvae are predators in soil systems. Above ground, adults contribute to pollination.

DESCRIPTION: Adults are soft bodied with leathery wing covers, and they have black, brown, yellow, or orange coloration. They resemble fireflies without light-emitting segments. They have glands at the end of their abdomen that secret defensive chemicals. Larvae are dark colored with elongated, flattened bodies that help them move with ease through soil and leaf litter while hunting with their sickle-shaped jaws.

WHERE THEY ARE FOUND: Adults are predominantly found on flowers or leaves, while larvae live in the upper soil layer, in litter, or under stones.

WHAT THEY EAT: Larvae and some adults eat insect eggs and larvae, aphids, snails, and slugs. Adults also consume pollen and nectar.

LIFE CYCLE: Soldier beetles lay eggs in moist soil or in leaf litter, having one or two generations a year. Larvae hunt for insects in loose soil and leaf litter, and under rocks, debris, or bark. Larvae overwinter in leaf litter, and pupation occurs just below the soil surface.

APPROX. NUMBER OF KNOWN SPECIES: 5,100 worldwide (470 in North America).

RELATIVE ABUNDANCE: Adults can congregate on flowers.

NOTES OF INTEREST:

- Soldier beetle larvae are coated with dense, short hairs that resemble velvet. These hairs are dark brown to purple, though the coats of species that eat aphids are pink.
- Adult soldier beetles can transfer pollen effectively. For example, *Chauliognathus pensylvanicus* can pollinate goldenrod (*Solidago* spp.).
- On-farm habitat can support adult soldier beetles. Reducing tillage and soil fumigants can support larvae. There is some evidence to suggest that larvae prefer areas with higher plant cover and humidity rather than bare ground, so areas of constant plant cover, such as those planted with cover crops or permanent plantings, may benefit larvae and their migration to nearby crops.

FIGURE 189—Goldenrod soldier beetle (*Chauliognathus pensylvanicus*) adult.

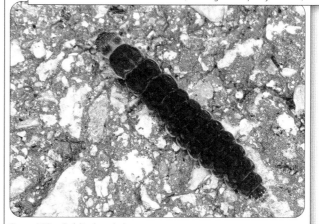
FIGURE 190—Soldier beetle larva.

FIGURE 191—Soldier beetle eggs.

SOFT-WINGED FLOWER BEETLES • NET-WINGED BEETLES

52. SOFT-WINGED FLOWER BEETLES

PHYLUM: Arthropoda » **CLASS:** Insecta »
 ORDER: Coleoptera » **FAMILY:** Melyridae
SIZE: 0.08–0.4" (2–10 mm).
ECOLOGICAL ROLE: The larvae of soft-winged flower beetles are predators in soil food webs.
DESCRIPTION: These small beetles have soft wing covers and an elongate, slightly ovular body that is brightly colored.
WHERE THEY ARE FOUND: Larvae are common in soil, in leaf litter, or under bark. Adults are frequently found on flowers, where they feed on other insects and pollen.
WHAT THEY EAT: Larvae prey on other invertebrates; adults eat insect eggs, pollen, or nectar.
LIFE CYCLE: Soft-winged flower beetles lay eggs in clusters in leaf litter, on the soil surface, or under bark. It is suspected that the beetles overwinter as eggs, larvae, or adults.
APPROX. NUMBER OF KNOWN SPECIES: 6,000 worldwide (520 in North America).
RELATIVE ABUNDANCE: Data unavailable.
NOTES OF INTEREST:
- Caterpillars, thrips, stink bug eggs, aphids, and spider mites are all prey for adult soft-winged flower beetles. Soft-winged flower beetles in the genus *Collops* are common predators of pests in cotton, sorghum, and alfalfa.

FIGURE 192—Adult soft-winged beetle adult.

FIGURE 193—Soft-winged beetle larva.

53. NET-WINGED BEETLES

PHYLUM: Arthropoda » **CLASS:** Insecta » **ORDER:** Coleoptera » **FAMILY:** Lycidae
SIZE: 0.2–0.7" (5–18 mm).
ECOLOGICAL ROLE: In soil systems, net-winged beetles are decomposers and may also be predators.
DESCRIPTION: Net-winged beetles have soft wings and resemble fireflies and soldier beetles. These beetles have raised edges running the length of their wing covers, have serrated antennae, and often have bright-orange or red color patterns on their body. Females are larger than males. Larvae look like they have armored plates, and their legs are well developed.
WHERE THEY ARE FOUND: Larvae occur on fungi, in rotting logs, under bark, or in leaf litter. Adults can be seen on flowers.
WHAT THEY EAT: Adult net-winged beetles consume nectar. Larvae feed on fungi and the juices of decaying plant materials but have also been reported to prey on small insects.

FIGURE 194—Adult net-winged beetle (*Plateros* sp.) adult.

LIFE CYCLE: Net-winged beetles deposit eggs in soil or decaying wood. Larvae and pupae may aggregate.

APPROX. NUMBER OF KNOWN SPECIES: 4,600 worldwide (80 in North America).

RELATIVE ABUNDANCE: Data unavailable.

NOTES OF INTEREST:

- Net-winged beetles are unpalatable to predators due to their consumption of toxic chemicals. They advertise their toxicity to birds and other predators through their bright body colors.
- Net-winged beetles will use a defensive strategy called reflex bleeding in which they exude stinky substances to deter predators.
- Some tiger moths, in the family Arctiidae, mimic the color patterns of these distasteful beetles, as do beetles in other beetle families.

FIGURE 195—Banded net-winged beetle (*Calopteron reticulatum*) larva.

54. ROVE BEETLES

PHYLUM: Arthropoda » CLASS: Insecta » ORDER: Coleoptera » FAMILY: Staphylinidae

SIZE: 0.03–1" (0.7–25 mm).

ECOLOGICAL ROLE: Rove beetles are important predators of soil life, contributing to the decomposition of plant and animal matter and some mixing of soil. They can also contribute to crop pest control.

DESCRIPTION: Rove beetles are black or brown in color with elongated, slender bodies and short wing covers. Species with shortest wing covers are those that spend the most time in the soil. Adults vary in size depending on species. Rove beetles are quick runners and fliers, and many curl the tip of their abdomen slightly upward as they run or when disturbed by potential predators. Larvae have elongated bodies and large, sickle-shaped jaws.

WHERE THEY ARE FOUND: Both larvae and adults are found in soil (primarily in upper layers, but some live in the deeper layers), mulch, leaf litter, fungi, or nests of ants, termites, mammals, or birds.

WHAT THEY EAT: Larvae and adults eat insect eggs and small larvae, slugs, and mites, and some also eat dead plant or animal matter.

LIFE CYCLE: Rove beetles lay eggs on leaves or under leaf litter. Pupae or adults overwinter under bark, and larvae overwinter under vegetation. Rove beetles may have one or multiple generations per year (it varies with species).

APPROX. NUMBER OF KNOWN SPECIES: 56,000 worldwide (4,400 in North America).

FIGURE 196—Adult rove beetle (*Platydracus* sp.).

FIGURE 197—Rove beetle larva.

RELATIVE ABUNDANCE: Rove beetles can be very abundant, and this group has the most species of any beetle family.

NOTES OF INTEREST:

- This group includes the short-winged mold beetles, also known as ant-loving beetles (Pselaphinae), most of which are predators of small arthropods such as dwarf millipedes, mites, springtails, and small worms rather than fungivores (as might be assumed from their common name).
- Some species of rove beetles are marine insects, living in sandy burrows in the intertidal zone of coastal areas. Female rove beetles of these species maintain a narrow burrow entrance to keep water out of the burrow during high tide.
- Conservation strategies for rove beetles include the creation of beetle banks (banked areas within fields planted with dense bunchgrasses) and wildflower field borders, limiting tillage and soil fumigants, and staggering harvest times of perennial forage crops such as alfalfa or clover.

55. GROUND BEETLES

PHYLUM: Arthropoda » **CLASS:** Insecta » **ORDER:** Coleoptera » **FAMILY:** Carabidae

SIZE: 0.12–1.2″ (3–30 mm).

ECOLOGICAL ROLE: Ground beetles fit into soil food webs in several ways. Ground beetles are predators as larvae and adults, and in agricultural systems they are important contributors to the control of crop pests. Some species will also eat detritus, fungi, and plant seeds.

DESCRIPTION: Ground beetle larvae are cream to brown in color and have a round head, hooked jaws, long legs, and bristly posterior projections. Adult ground beetles range in size from small to large and have threadlike antennae; prominent eyes; a head narrower than their thorax; an extended, oval abdomen; and ridged wing covers. Adults' coloration is dark and shiny, usually black or brown, with some species having green, blue, or purple iridescence. On farms, ground beetles prey on crop pests and consume weed seeds.

WHERE THEY ARE FOUND: Ground beetles can be found under debris, stones, and logs; in soil cracks and leaf litter; and on the soil surface or vegetation. Larvae most often live in soil, burrows, and leaf litter, or on the surface.

WHAT THEY EAT: Larvae and adults eat insects—including caterpillars, grasshoppers, beetles, aphids, and flies—as well as snails and slugs. Most ground beetles feed nocturnally, though some species are active during the day. Adults tend to feed at the soil surface or on vegetation. Predaceous larvae usually feed under the soil surface on rootworms, caterpillars, and other soft-bodied insects. The larvae and adults of some species of ground beetles are omnivorous and will also eat carrion or fungi, while others feed primarily on seeds of several common weeds.

LIFE CYCLE: Ground beetles lay eggs singly or in small batches in crevices or, more frequently, in the soil; females of some species may guard their brood. They produce one generation a year, with adults living up to four years.

FIGURE 198—Ground beetle adult.

FIGURE 199—Ground beetle (*Dicaelus* sp.) larva eating a snail.

APPROX. NUMBER OF KNOWN SPECIES: 34,000 worldwide (2,500 in North America).

RELATIVE ABUNDANCE: Data unavailable.

NOTES OF INTEREST:

- Ground beetles seize their prey using their mandibles, and then they cover their prey with digestive juices before eventually ingesting them.
- Ground beetle communities can be associated with plant communities.
- Beetle banks—earthen ridges within fields planted with bunchgrasses—can provide important overwintering habitat for ground beetles. Avoid excessive tillage or burning of crop residue, as these practices can impact multiple life stages of these beetles and reduce populations quickly. Weed seed predators are more often found in fields with surface residue rather than bare, fallow fields.
- A classic British study comparing insecticide-treated and untreated fields found that cabbage fields treated with insecticide had greater crop damage from root maggots (flies in the family Anthomyiidae) because more than 30 species of predatory ground beetles had been killed.

FIGURE 200—Beetle bank of bunchgrasses.

- Both larvae and adult ground beetles can eat up to 2.5× their body weight in prey per day. The average daily food consumption is 0.875 grams for a body weight of 0.640 grams. Larvae are known to kill more prey than they can eat.

56. TIGER BEETLES

PHYLUM: Arthropoda » CLASS: Insecta » ORDER: Coleoptera » FAMILY: Carabidae » SUBFAMILY: Cicindelinae

SIZE: 0.24–1.57" (6–40 mm).

ECOLOGICAL ROLE: Tiger beetles are predators; adults actively hunt at the soil surface, while larvae wait within a burrow to snatch their prey. These beetles are also burrowers, with larvae excavating soil burrows as deep as 18" (45 cm).

DESCRIPTION: Tiger beetle larvae anchor their bodies within their vertical burrows, concealing their large jaws under their flat heads while waiting for prey to wander near. Adult tiger beetles may be grayish-brown, metallic bronze, or iridescent blue or green, sometimes with white markings on their wing covers. Adult tiger beetles have large eyes, often have hairs on their faces, and have long, slender legs.

WHERE THEY ARE FOUND: Tiger beetles favor open ground, such as road shoulders and woodland paths, as well as sandy areas like lake or stream edges and dunes. Adult tiger beetles are extremely fast-moving and hunt and chase their prey on the surface of the ground. Tiger beetle larvae typically hunt from cylindrical burrows. Most tiger beetles hunt during the day, though some are active at dusk or are nocturnal.

WHAT THEY EAT: Larvae and adults eat arthropods found on the soil surface.

LIFE CYCLE: Female tiger beetles excavate burrows 3.94–5.9" (10–15 cm) deep in damp, well-drained soil, in which they lay eggs individually. Larvae expand the burrow as they grow and may take two to three years to reach adulthood. They overwinter as larvae in the soil or as adults in grass clumps.

FIGURE 201—Tiger beetle adult.

GROUND BEETLES • TIGER BEETLES

FIGURE 202—Tiger beetle larva burrow, viewed from outside.

FIGURE 203—Tiger beetle larva inside and outside burrow (J. Nardi 2007.)

TIGER BEETLES

APPROX. NUMBER OF KNOWN SPECIES: 1,300 worldwide (120 in North America).
RELATIVE ABUNDANCE: Data unavailable.
NOTES OF INTEREST:

- Three species of tiger beetle are endangered (e.g., Salt Creek tiger beetle, *Cicindela nevadica lincolniana*), and two are threatened.
- Adults and larvae have excellent eyesight.
- They are among the fastest insects—recorded at 5.6 mph (9 kph)—and take flight after running quickly.
- Tiger beetle larvae uses hooks on their abdomen to anchor themselves within their burrows.

57. VARIEGATED MUD-LOVING BEETLES

PHYLUM: Arthropoda » **CLASS:** Insecta » **ORDER:** Coleoptera » **FAMILY:** Heteroceridae
SIZE: 0.04–0.3" (1–8 mm).
ECOLOGICAL ROLE: Variegated mud-loving beetles move and mix soil, excavating winding burrows. They may also contribute to plant decomposition.
DESCRIPTION: As adults, these small beetles have flattened black or brown bodies with mustard-yellow bands or spots. They have legs with spines used for excavating earth, as well as powerful jaws and short, clubbed antennae.
WHERE THEY ARE FOUND: Adults and larvae dig burrows in the muddy soil of stream banks or near ponds. Adults are active at night but will also fly from their burrows if flooding occurs.
WHAT THEY EAT: These beetles consume plant matter, algae, plankton, and organic debris.
LIFE CYCLE: Variegated mud-loving beetles lay small masses of eggs in a chamber in the soil. Pupation also occurs in the soil.

FIGURE 204—Variegated mud-loving beetle (*Heterocerus sp.*).

APPROX. NUMBER OF KNOWN SPECIES: 500 worldwide (40 in the United States).
RELATIVE ABUNDANCE: These beetles can be very abundant on the shores of ponds or stream banks.
NOTES OF INTEREST:

- These beetles are coated with dense hairs that repel water and mud, allowing them to avoid getting stuck in mud.
- Variegated mud-loving beetles are important prey for birds and frogs.
- It is very difficult to distinguish species of these beetles using external characteristics, and anatomy of the male genitals is typically used to separate species (it remains nearly impossible to identify the species of females).

58. GRUBS OF SCARAB BEETLES AND WEEVILS

PHYLUM: Arthropoda » **CLASS:** Insecta » **ORDER:** Coleoptera »
  FAMILIES: Scarabaeidae » SUBFAMILIES: Dynastinae, Melolonthinae, Rutelinae;
    Curculionidae » SUBFAMILY: Entiminae

SIZE: 0.08–4.7" (2 mm–12 cm).

ECOLOGICAL ROLE: The larvae, also known as grubs, of scarab beetles and weevils are herbivores, eating plant roots in the soil. They are also burrowers, moving up and down in the soil based on season and precipitation. Though they cause damage to plants, they also improve soil structure as they move around.

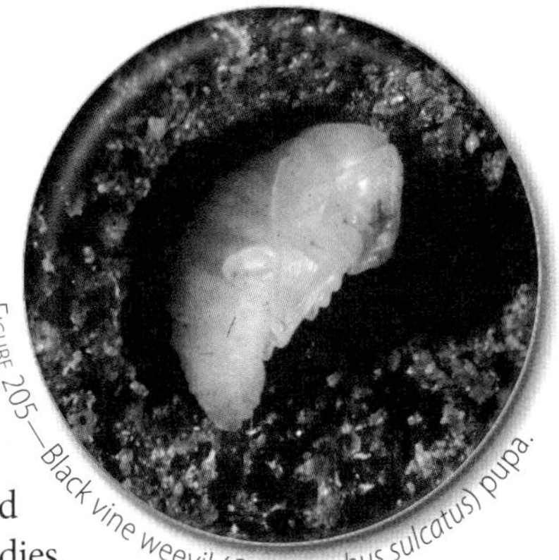

FIGURE 205—Black vine weevil (*Otiorhynchus sulcatus*) pupa.

DESCRIPTION: Scarab beetle grubs have hard, brown heads with soft, white, C-shaped bodies. In adults, scarab beetle size and color patterns can vary, but all have oval bodies and clubbed antennae, and they often have scalloped front legs. Root weevil grubs are legless and have hard, dark heads and white, soft, cylindrical bodies. Adult weevils are small, are usually drab in color, and have an elongated snout and elbowed antennae.

WHERE THEY ARE FOUND: Scarab beetle grubs and weevil grubs are found among plant roots at various depths in the soil. Adults live above ground and are frequently found on plants.

WHAT THEY EAT: Scarab beetles and weevils—adults and larvae—are herbivorous: grubs consume the roots of plants, and adults feed on foliage. Weevil larvae and adults often share the same host plant.

LIFE CYCLE: These insects lay eggs on soil. Larvae then burrow into the soil. Some species mature in a single year, while others feed on roots as larvae for several years—up to five years in cold climates. Larvae overwinter.

APPROX. NUMBER OF KNOWN SPECIES: More than 16,600 scarab beetle grubs (850 in North America) and about 50,000 root weevils worldwide (124 genera in North America).

RELATIVE ABUNDANCE: Beetle grubs can be very abundant. Japanese beetles (*Popillia japonica*), a scarab beetle introduced in the United States, are found at average densities of 175 per square yard (heavy infestations are 1,500 per square yard). Root weevils were found at densities of up to 463 per square meter in a German forest.

NOTES OF INTEREST:

- Weevils are a highly diverse group of beetles (which is truly something, given how diverse beetles are). According to James Nardi, in his book *Life in the Soil*, "Different weevils feed on different plant parts, and every plant part is eaten by some weevil somewhere."
- Some herbivorous scarabs and root weevils, such as the strawberry root weevil (*Otiorhynchus ovatus*) are agricultural pests.
- The largest beetles in the world are scarab beetles in the genus *Goliathus*, found in Africa. Other exceptionally large scarab beetles are Hercules beetles (*Dynastes*) and rhinoceros beetles (*Xyloryctes*).

FIGURE 206—Scarab beetle grub.

FIGURE 207—Carrot beetle (*Tomarus gibbosus*) adult.

59. CLICK BEETLES (OR WIREWORMS)

PHYLUM: Arthropoda » **CLASS:** Insecta » **ORDER:** Coleoptera » **FAMILY:** Elateridae

SIZE: Larvae are 0.39–2.4" (1–6 cm) and adults are 0.06–1.6" (1.5 mm–4 cm).

ECOLOGICAL ROLE: Click beetles are decomposers, herbivores, or predators and move lots of nutrients through food webs.

DESCRIPTION: Click beetle larvae—often referred to as wireworms—have elongate, hardened bodies covered with sensory bristles. Adults are brown, gray, or black and have a flexible joint that helps them to bend and snap their bodies. These beetles have serrated antennae and elongated bodies that are rounded at both ends.

WHERE THEY ARE FOUND: Larvae are associated with dead wood or leaf litter, or they dwell in soil, including in cultivated fields. Adults can be found on vegetation or under bark.

WHAT THEY EAT: Some species eat plant debris, while others prey on other arthropods; root-feeding wireworms can damage crops by chewing on roots, and they are pests in crops such as corn, carrots, and potatoes.

LIFE CYCLE: Larvae spend three to seven years underground and may go through nine to 15 instars before pupating in the ground, in dead wood, or under bark. Development time varies with species, nutrition, and climate.

APPROX. NUMBER OF KNOWN SPECIES: 9,000 worldwide (900 in North America).

RELATIVE ABUNDANCE: Data unavailable.

NOTES OF INTEREST:

FIGURE 208—Eyed click beetle (*Alaus oculatus* sp.) adult.

FIGURE 209—Click beetle larva.

- Their common name comes from the audible click sound that occurs when an adult beetle flexes and then straightens its body, propelling itself into the air. This action allows click beetles to flip themselves over if they are ever on their backs.

- Wireworms (larval stage) spend much of their life in the soil.
- The damage threshold in crops is generally about 100,000 larvae per acre. Soil sampling or baiting can help determine wireworm presence.

60. DUNG BEETLES

PHYLUM: Arthropoda » **CLASS:** Insecta » **ORDER:** Coleoptera » **FAMILIES:** Geotrupidae, Scarabaeidae » **SUBFAMILIES:** Aphodiinae, Scarabaeinae

SIZE: 0.08–1.2" (2 mm–3 cm).

ECOLOGICAL ROLE: Dung beetles are scavengers and decomposers, transforming manure to humus and speeding up the process of returning nutrients to the soil. These beetles are particularly important to the cattle industry; their work enhances forage palatability, recycles nitrogen, and reduces pest and parasite habitat. Dung beetles' ecosystem services to agriculture are easily worth more than $380 million annually. This figure, from Losey and Vaughan (2003), is an estimate of the losses to producers in the cattle industry due to forage fouling, nitrogen volatilization, parasitism, and pest flies that were averted because of the work of dung beetles. This number is an underestimate because dung beetles also provide their recycling services to other rangeland and pasture-raised animals (e.g. bison, dairy cattle, sheep, horses, and more). These beetles make burrows, digging nests to 23.6" (60 cm) deep or more, and they disperse seeds present in dung. Additionally, dung beetles can reduce food-borne pathogens on crops by disrupting dung-feeding flies that are vectors of the pathogens.

DESCRIPTION: Adults have oval, convex bodies that are dull black, but some are shiny black and a few are metallic green to copper. They have clubbed antennae and toothed or scalloped front legs. Larvae have hard heads and white, soft bodies that are curved in a C-shape.

WHERE THEY ARE FOUND: Larvae are found within dung or within nests provisioned with dung, and adults are found near dung in many habitats, including grasslands, forests, farmlands, and deserts.

WHAT THEY EAT: These beetles feed on the waste of mammals, particularly herbivores. The dung of herbivores contains partially digested plant material, and the adults feed on the dung juices while the larvae feed on the fibrous content.

LIFE CYCLE: The odor of fresh dung attracts adult beetles that fly to it in order to collect food for their young. Some beetles excavate a tunnel for a nest immediately below the dung; from the main shaft, females will dig brood chambers and deposit an egg in each, along with pieces of dung. Others lay their eggs within the pat of dung. A few species will roll a portion of the dung away from the pat before concealing the ball underground. Dung beetle larvae munch through their weight in dung each day until they reach pupation. Life spans can extend up to three years.

APPROX. NUMBER OF KNOWN SPECIES: 5,000 worldwide (550 in North America).

RELATIVE ABUNDANCE: Diversity is lowest in highly altered landscapes, but a few common generalist species can be very abundant in areas like pastures.

NOTES OF INTEREST:

- The burial of dung changes the nutrients available in the soil, increasing phosphate, nitrate, sulfur, and carbon.
- Dung beetles are highly efficient; for example, within prairies without introduced grazers, dung beetles can completely remove the dung of native mammals (e.g., deer and coyote) in one to two days.
- Organic farming tends to promote dung beetle diversity compared to conventional farming. In a study on food-safety risks, dung beetles on organic farms removed dung more effectively and suppressed human pathogenic *E. coli*.
- Dung beetles were sacred to ancient Egyptians, who saw dung beetles rolling their dung as earthly

FIGURE 210—Humpback dung beetles (*Deltochilum gibbosum*) rolling a ball.

FIGURE 211—Rainbow scarab (*Phanaeus vindex*) adult male digging burrow.

FIGURE 212—Dung beetle larva and pupa.

manifestations of the sun god Ra escorting the sun to the horizon each day. Dung beetles were also attributed with the power to be reborn after death, based on observations of adult beetles emerging wholly from the ground after the pupal stage, which was perceived as death.

- Pesticides used to treat cattle for parasites can have detrimental impacts on dung beetles. Synthetic pyrethroids are less damaging than macrocyclic lactone pesticides, but farms that use them still have reduced abundance of some species. Loss of dung colonizers may delay dung pat decomposition.

- Dung beetles contribute to a number of ecological processes, including nutrient cycling, plant productivity and growth, soil mixing, secondary seed dispersal, and control of flies and parasites.
- Agroforestry practices may support a greater diversity of dung beetles on farms because they contribute to habitat heterogeneity.

- Annually, dung beetles can bury a ton of dung on 2.5 acres (1 hectare) of soil.
- Dung beetles try to steal balls or usurp pats from one another—dung is a valuable resource!
- Dung beetles that consume kangaroo dung do not find dung of other grazers palatable. In Australia, dung of introduced grazers began to overtake pastures, and so dung beetles that consumed cattle, horse, and sheep dung were introduced.

61. HISTER BEETLES

PHYLUM: Arthropoda » **CLASS:** Insecta » **ORDER:** Coleoptera » **FAMILY:** Histeridae
SIZE: 0.02–0.39" (0.5–10 mm).
ECOLOGICAL ROLE: Hister beetles are predators of insects and other arthropods. These beetles are particularly known for reducing fly maggots in dung and carrion. They are allies for ranchers and producers.
DESCRIPTION: Adult hister beetles have black, glossy oval bodies, with wing covers that cut off squarely, leaving several abdominal segments visible. They have elbowed antennae and spines on their legs. Larvae have large, hard jaws and a soft, cream-colored body, with tiny legs that are disproportionately small for their body size.
WHERE THEY ARE FOUND: These beetles are found near decaying matter, including dung, carrion, and fungi; under the bark of logs; in leaf litter; within the nests of ants, termites, or birds; or in mammal burrows. Their habitats are widespread, ranging from farmland to grassland to forests—anywhere they can live in close proximity to their prey.

FIGURE 213—Hister beetle (*Hister* sp.) adult carrying mites.

WHAT THEY EAT: Hister beetle adults and larvae consume the insects that live in decaying materials, such as fly maggots and pupae.
LIFE CYCLE: These insects lay eggs near a food source (e.g., in dung) that adults locate through odor. Larvae and pupal stages can develop fairly quickly, and hister beetles can develop from egg to adult in less than 30 days. Adults can live for two to three years.
APPROX. NUMBER OF KNOWN SPECIES: 4,000 worldwide (about 500 in North America).
RELATIVE ABUNDANCE: Data unavailable.
NOTES OF INTEREST:

- *Carcinops pumilio* has been studied for its use in controlling flies in manure in poultry production, as an augmentative biological control agent.
- Dung beetles and carrion beetles benefit from the presence of hister beetles, who reduce competition with fly maggots.
- Hister beetles will pretend to be dead if they feel at risk.

- Hister beetles often carry predatory mites on their bodies, dispersing the mites wherever they go. These mites also often consume fly eggs and maggots.

FIGURE 214—Hister beetle (*Hister* sp.) larva.

DUNG BEETLES · HISTER BEETLES

62. CARRION BEETLES AND BURYING BEETLES

PHYLUM: Arthropoda » CLASS: Insecta » ORDER: Coleoptera » FAMILY: Silphidae » SUBFAMILIES: Nicrophorinae, Silphinae

SIZE: 0.47–1.6" (1.2–4 cm).

ECOLOGICAL ROLE: Carrion beetles and burying beetles are the primary arthropods that contribute to the decomposition of animal carcasses. Carcasses decompose significantly slower without their work.

DESCRIPTION: Adults are large and brightly colored beetles with clubbed antennae. Carrion beetles (Silphinae) have a broadly oval, slightly flattened body and are mostly black, with yellow or orange markings. Burying beetles (Nicrophorinae) are primarily black, with red or orange patterns on their wing covers and brightly colored antennae. The carrion beetles in the genus *Silpha* are dark brown or black, with bright yellow on their thorax. Carrion and burying beetle larvae are dark and appear as if they are attired with armored plates.

WHERE THEY ARE FOUND: Carrion beetles and burying beetles are found near, under, or in the bodies of dead animals; they occur in a variety of habitats. A few species are found either on fungi or in ant nests.

WHAT THEY EAT: Burying beetles excavate beneath the bodies of small vertebrate animals, causing the body to sink into the ground. Carrion beetles consume carrion as it lies. Carrion and burying beetles can detect the odor of carrion from great distances and are strong fliers.

LIFE CYCLE: Burying and carrion beetles lay their eggs on or near animal carcasses. Carrion beetles are found on unburied bodies of large dead mammals such as raccoons, horses, and cows. Only burying beetles bury dead animals. Larvae and adults feed on carrion; larvae and adults of some carrion beetles will also feed on fly larvae and other beetle larvae. Female burying beetles will feed regurgitated carrion to their newly hatched larvae. Pupation of burying beetles occurs in the soil near the chamber with the carcass. Carrion beetles also pupate in the soil, and adults overwinter.

APPROX. NUMBER OF KNOWN SPECIES: 215 worldwide (30 in North America).

RELATIVE ABUNDANCE: These beetles are typically in low in abundance, but multiple species co-occur.

NOTES OF INTEREST:
- Burying beetles may need to move a carcass several feet in order to find a suitable place to dig (they are very strong). There is a great deal of competition for dead bodies, and so speed in burying the body is essential. A breeding pair works together to bury and prepare a dead body, and this biparental care is pretty unique among insects.

FIGURE 215—American carrion beetle (*Necrophila americana*).

FIGURE 216—Roundneck sexton burying beetle (*Nicrophorus orbicollis*).

FIGURE 217—Burying beetle (*Heterosilpha* sp.) larva.

- Burying beetles prefer birds and small mammals over large mammals.
- Burying beetles reduce competition with other carrion decomposers by killing fly eggs and maggots on or in the carrion. There are also predatory mites (e.g., in the genus *Poecilochirus*) that hitch rides on carrion beetles, dropping off the beetles when at a new carcass to consume small carrion consumers like flies.

These mites will then climb back on to the beetles to be transported to another carcass.
- The American burying beetle (*Nicrophorus americanus*) is a federally registered endangered species. Once present in at least 35 states, it now has populations in only six states (Rhode Island, Arkansas, Kansas, Oklahoma, Nebraska, and Massachusetts).

63. DERMESTID BEETLES (OR HIDE BEETLES AND CARPET BEETLES)

PHYLUM: Arthropoda » **CLASS:** Insecta » **ORDER:** Coleoptera » **FAMILY:** Dermestidae
SIZE: 0.08–0.47" (2–12 mm).
ECOLOGICAL ROLE: Hide beetles are scavengers, feeding on a variety of animal and plant tissues, and assist in the decomposition process.

DESCRIPTION: Adults have oval, convex bodies that are usually gray, brown, or black, sometimes with color patterns, and they are covered in fine scales or short hairs. Their antennae are short and clubbed, and they have chewing mouthparts. Larvae of these beetles are often brown and covered with long hairs or tufts of hairs.

WHERE THEY ARE FOUND: Larvae and adults are found on animal carcasses, as well as in nests of insects, birds, and mammals. Adults of some species can be found on flowers.

WHAT THEY EAT: Hide beetles consume animal skin, fur, feathers, and carrion. In built environments, they also will eat stored grains or wool, silk, cotton, and more—earning them another common name: carpet beetles.

LIFE CYCLE: Development time from egg to adult varies with species; some hide beetles develop into adults within six weeks, while other species may take nearly a year.

APPROX. NUMBER OF KNOWN SPECIES: 1,000 worldwide (120 in North America).

RELATIVE ABUNDANCE: Data unavailable.

NOTES OF INTEREST:
- The larvae can digest keratin, found in hair and feathers.
- Hide beetles are used in museums to clean off vertebrate skeletons and in forensic entomology to estimate the age of corpses.
- These beetles are the bane of insect collections, as they can destroy dead, pinned insects in very little time.
- Several species of hide beetle are economic pests, causing significant damage to stored products such as grains and seeds, dried meats and cheeses, and materials of animal origin like wool, fur, and silk.

FIGURE 218—Fringed larder beetle (*Dermestes frischi*) adult.

FIGURE 219—Dermestid beetle larva on an animal carcass.

CARRION BEETLES AND BURYING BEETLES · DERMESTID BEETLES

64. SAP BEETLES

PHYLUM: Arthropoda » **CLASS:** Insecta » **ORDER:** Coleoptera » **FAMILY:** Nitidulidae
SIZE: 0.04–0.59" (1–15 mm).
ECOLOGICAL ROLE: Sap beetles are decomposers and fungivores in soil food webs.
DESCRIPTION: Adults have oval or elongate bodies, short wing covers that leave the end of the abdomen exposed, and clubbed antennae. They are often dark in color, sometimes with mustard-yellow markings. Larvae have white, cylindrical bodies with a brown head.
WHERE THEY ARE FOUND: Sap beetles are found beneath bark of dead stumps or logs, near fungi and sap, rotting fruit.
WHAT THEY EAT: Larvae and adults consume fungi but also eat flowing sap and decaying fruits, and some feed on carrion. Some adults also eat nectar or pollen.
LIFE CYCLE: Sap beetles lay eggs near a food source. Pupation occurs in the ground. Development time is fairly short, and there can be multiple generations per year.
APPROX. NUMBER OF KNOWN SPECIES: 4,500 worldwide (165 in North America).
RELATIVE ABUNDANCE: Sap beetles can be concentrated in areas with food sources. For example, picnic beetles (*Glischrochilus* spp.) can aggregate at certain sites.
NOTES OF INTEREST:

FIGURE 220—Sap beetle (*Omosita colon*) adult.

FIGURE 221—Sap beetle larva.

- The dusky sap beetle (*Carpophilus lugubris*) is a pest of sweet corn—the larvae feed at the tip of an ear of corn and are often missed during the canning process.
- Some species wait by ant trails at night to scare ants into regurgitating their food, which the beetles then pillage.
- Small hive beetle (*Aethina tumida*), a species introduced in the United States, causes damage to honey bee hives.

65. BEETLES ASSOCIATED WITH LOGS

A number of beetles dine on and reside in rotting logs. These beetles are important decomposers, helping to break down dead wood. Wood fibers like cellulose are difficult to break down, and these beetles often have bacteria, fungi, or protozoa in their digestive tracts that aid in digestion.

BESS BEETLES (Passalidae) are large, measuring 1.2–1.57" (30–40 mm). They have shiny, black bodies—bess beetles are also known as patent leather beetles—and longitudinal grooves on their wing covers. They have a square-shaped thorax, clubbed antennae, a horn on their head, and large mandibles. Larvae are large white grubs that assume a C-shape posture when not active. Bess beetles live in rotting logs, within galleries in family

FIGURE 222—Bess beetle adult.

BEETLES ASSOCIATED WITH LOGS

FIGURE 223—Eastern bess beetle (*Odontotaenius disjunctus*) colony nursery.

FIGURE 224—Adult giant stag beetle (*Lucanus elaphus*) adult.

groups of larvae and adults—unusual for beetles. Adults provide care for their young, preparing and feeding them decaying wood. They only consume wood where fungi and bacteria are present, breaking down the wood, to aid in their digestion. After pupation, young beetles leave their parent log to mate and colonize a new log. Adults produce squeaking noises (rubbing the undersides of their wings across roughened areas on the back of their abdomen) that help them stay in touch with each other. There are at least 14 calls, including mating calls and signals of distress.

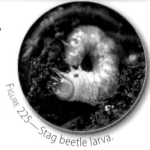

FIGURE 225—Stag beetle larva.

STAG BEETLES (Lucanidae) are also quite large in size, measuring 0.59–1.58" (1.5–4 cm), with similar body shapes as bess beetles. Some male stag beetles have large mandibles that are nearly half as long as their body, often with branches like a stag. These mandibles are used in vying for territory and mates. Larvae reside in decaying wood, feeding on its juices and associated fungi. Stag beetles may spend up to six years as larvae.

FALSE CLICK BEETLES (Eucnemidae) are small, measuring 0.39" (10 mm) or less, and are brown, resembling click beetles in appearance. Adults quiver their antennae almost constantly, and some, like click beetles, can click and jump. Their larvae are legless and eyeless, and they tend to bore across the grain of dead wood. Larvae have preferences for wood that has just begun to decay.

FIGURE 226—False click beetle larva.

FIGURE 227—False click beetle adults.

TOE-WINGED BEETLES (Ptilodactylidae) are small, measuring 0.16–0.24" (4–6 mm), with brown, elongate, oval bodies and long, serrated antennae. Their head is not generally

FIGURE 228—Toe-winged beetle larva.

FIGURE 229—Toe-winged beetle (*Ptilodactyla* sp.) adult.

visible from above. Larvae occur in and consume damp wood or decaying vegetation, and adults are found on vegetation, often near streams. Some larvae are aquatic.

The **TELEPHONE-POLE BEETLE** (*Micromalthus debilis*) is a beetle species found in eastern North America and is the only living species in an otherwise extinct family. They are small, measuring 0.06–0.1" (1.5–2.5 mm), and dark in color, with large eyes that protrude on the sides of their head. Larvae feed on moist, decaying wood—primarily oak and chestnut logs (but also rotting telephone poles, hence their common name). Unusually, these beetles give birth as larvae and without mating. They are the only known beetle with this reproductive strategy.

FIGURE 230—Telephone-pole beetle adult.

66. BEETLES ASSOCIATED WITH FUNGI

There are many different groups of beetles that consume the fruiting bodies, spores, or hyphae of fungi. Living in leaf litter, under bark of dead trees, and within decaying vegetation, these beetles incidentally transport spores of fungi, helping in fungal dispersal.

Beetles that are associated with fungi include:
- Minute fungus beetles (Corylophidae)
- Handsome fungus beetles (Endomychidae)
- Pleasing fungus beetles (Erotylidae)
- Feather-winged beetles (Ptiliidae)
- Silken fungus beetles (Cryptophagidae)
- Minute brown scavenger beetles (Latridiidae)
- Hairy fungus beetles (Mycetophagidae)
- Minute tree-fungus beetles (Ciidae)
- False darkling beetles (Melandryidae)
- Some species of darkling beetles (Tenebrionidae)
- Round fungus beetles (Leiodidae), and others

The number of beetle species associated with fungi is estimated to be at least 80,000 worldwide.

FIGURE 231—Pretty handsome fungus beetle (*Phymaphora pulchella*) adult.

FIGURE 232—Minute tree-fungus beetles (*Cis* sp.) adults.

FIGURE 233—Featherwing beetle adult.

FIGURE 234—Adult darkling beetle (*Bolitophagus corticola*) feeding on fungus.

FIGURE 235—Pleasing blue fungus beetle (*Gibbifer californicus*) adult feeding on fungus and larva preparing to pupate (inset).

ANTS, BEES, AND WASPS (HYMENOPTERA) are part of a diverse order of insects that includes groups that are of great importance to soil life as movers of soil, predators, and parasitoids. Ants, bees, predatory wasps, and parasitoid wasps have narrow, waist-like constrictions; two pairs of membranous wings; and long, threadlike antennae.

67. ANTS

PHYLUM: Arthropoda » **CLASS:** Insecta » **ORDER:** Hymenoptera » **FAMILY:** Formicidae

SIZE: 0.04–0.98" (1–25 mm).

ECOLOGICAL ROLE: Ants are among the most significant insect groups in soil. They move a great deal of soil and influence soil structure, and they are predators of small invertebrates. Ants are also important seed dispersers.

DESCRIPTION: Ants are red, brown, or black. Between their thorax and abdomen, they have a constricted waist with one or two upright lobes. Their antennae are elbowed (the first segment is very long). Queens are larger than workers and have wings, though they shed these after mating. Males are winged and are much smaller than queens.

WHERE THEY ARE FOUND: Ant colonies can be on the soil surface in leaf litter or dead wood, with a few species nesting inside trees, but the majority of ants in North America nest underground. Ants construct extensive nests with chambers and tunnels and excavate quite a lot of soil, adding a great variety of organic matter. Ants occur in all terrestrial habitats—they are found as far and wide as the Arctic and oceanic islands.

WHAT THEY EAT: Many species are carnivorous on small arthropods or are scavengers of dead animals; others feed on plants, sap, nectar, or honeydew, and some eat fungi.

LIFE CYCLE: All ant species are truly social insects. They live in complex colonies, nesting with a queen who reproduces, workers who perform specific roles (e.g., guard, forage, or nurse), and overlapping generations. Males and queens are produced in large numbers at one time of the year; they then emerge from colonies and mate, and males die quickly after. The mated queen locates a suitable nesting site and produces her brood; once workers emerge, they take over care of the colony. Colonies are perennial and may persist for several years. Colonies vary in size from 12 to thousands and can be complex in structure and organization. Ants secrete substances that act as odor trails or alarms to stimulate activity.

APPROX. NUMBER OF KNOWN SPECIES: 14,000 worldwide (700 in North America).

RELATIVE ABUNDANCE: Ants are among the most abundant insects in the world and outnumber most other terrestrial animals; about 1% of all insect individuals are ants.

NOTES OF INTEREST:

- Ants occur on all continents except Antarctica, and their diversity is highest in tropical areas. The biomass

FIGURE 236—*Aphaenogaster* worker ants carrying a queen.

FIGURE 237—Male *Aphaenogaster* ant.

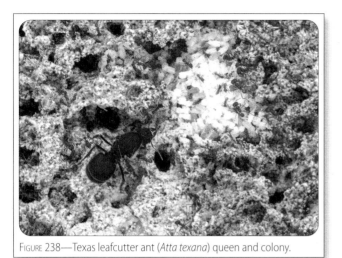

FIGURE 238—Texas leafcutter ant (*Atta texana*) queen and colony.

FIGURE 239—Allegheny mound ant (*Formica exsectoides*) nest.

of ants in rainforests is equal to or greater than the biomass of all vertebrates in the rainforest combined.

- Some ants have a stinger (a modified ovipositor) but some have lost the stinger and spray formic acid in defense. All ants may bite.
- Some ants have a symbiotic relationship with aphids, protecting them from harm or transporting them between plants and, in return, feeding on the honeydew (the sugary secretions) the aphids provide.
- Harvester ants (*Pogonomyrmex* spp.) in the U.S. desert Southwest carry approximately 15 million seeds per acre per year, which is about 1% of the total seed crop.
- Some seeds have fleshy structures, called elaiosomes, which entice ants to carry the seeds long distances. Ants will consume the elaiosomes, which contain lots of nutrients.
- There are more than 40 introduced species of ants in the United States, and some are major pests on farms (e.g., red imported fire ants aggressively defend their nests) while others are pests in cities (e.g., Argentine ants invade homes looking for food).
- In the southwestern United States, harvester ant galleries can be as deep as 15' (4.6 m) underground. Workers of another desert ant move 150–300 lb. (68–16 kg) of subsoil to the surface for every anthill they construct!
- Ants in a Massachusetts field moved enough soil in one year to cover the field with a 0.19" (5 mm) layer, adding up to 30 tons per acre.

FIGURE 240—Harvester ants (*Pogonomyrmex* sp.) carrying seeds to their nest.

- Rove, hister, feather-winged, and short-winged mold beetles may all be found in ant colonies, as well as mites, cockroaches, and bristletails. These visitors are referred to as inquilines, and benefit from living in close proximity to the ants without causing them harm.
- In the eastern United States, mound-building ants (*Formica* spp.) create earthworks of 2–3' (0.61–0.91 m) in diameter and often as high.
- Tillage can reduce ant numbers and ant predation on crop pests.

ANTS

68. SCARAB-HUNTING WASPS

PHYLUM: Arthropoda » **CLASS:** Insecta » **ORDER:** Hymenoptera » **FAMILIES:** Scoliidae, Tiphiidae

SIZE: Scoliid wasps: 0.79–2" (20–50 mm); Tiphiid wasps: 0.24–0.98" (6–25 mm).

ECOLOGICAL ROLE: Scarab-hunting wasps are external parasitoids, helping to control scarab beetle populations, and also move earth as they dig to find their hosts.

DESCRIPTION: There are two main groups of scarab-hunting wasps: scoliid wasps and tiphiid wasps. Adult scoliid wasps are large, robust wasps that have spiny, bristly legs. Their bodies are often black with bright orange, yellow, or red colorations, and their wings are darkened or metallic blue-black. Tiphiid wasps have slender bodies and elongated abdomens. Most tiphiid wasps are black, though some also have yellow markings. Females of some tiphiid species may be wingless.

WHERE THEY ARE FOUND: Scarab-hunting wasp larvae are found in the soil, developing on their beetle hosts. Adults are found on flowers or searching grassy areas for beetle grubs.

WHAT THEY EAT: These wasp larvae are parasitoids of beetle larvae, particularly scarab beetles, including Japanese beetles. The adult female wasps search fields and lawns for beetle grubs, and when they detect them, dig down through the soil to the grub, paralyze it, lay an egg on it, and leave the grub for their young to devour. Sometimes these wasps will paralyze grubs without leaving eggs, and grubs do not recover from the sting. Adults consume nectar.

LIFE CYCLE: Scarab-hunting wasps lay eggs next to their beetle hosts, and larvae develop on hosts. Pupae overwinter in soil. Ten to 12 months pass between egg deposition and emergence of adults, and there is one generation per year.

APPROX. NUMBER OF KNOWN SPECIES: 560 scoliid wasps worldwide (20 in North America) and 1,500 tiphiid wasps worldwide (200 in North America).

RELATIVE ABUNDANCE: Data unavailable.

NOTES OF INTEREST:

• Incorporating nectar-producing flowers into the landscape can increase these wasps' parasitism of beetle grubs.

FIGURE 241—Scoliid wasp adult drinking nectar from a flower.

FIGURE 242—Hairy-footed scoliid wasp (*Campsomeris pilipes*) digging in soil, hunting for prey.

FIGURE 243—Tiphiid wasp larva (outlined) parasitizing Oriental beetle grub.

FIGURE 244—Five-banded tiphiid wasp (*Myzinum quinquecincta*) adult.

69. GROUND-NESTING BEES

PHYLUM: Arthropoda » **CLASS:** Insecta » **ORDER:** Hymenoptera » **FAMILIES:** Andrenidae, Apidae, Colletidae, Halictidae, Melittidae

SIZE: 0.16–0.79" (4–20 mm).

ECOLOGICAL ROLE: Ground-nesting bees are critically important pollinators of wild plants and many crops. These bees are diggers, moving and aerating soil as they construct nests in which their young will develop. Some nests are shallow—only a few centimeters deep—while others may be a 3.3' (1 m) or more deep.

DESCRIPTION: Ground-nesting bees have two pairs of wings, threadlike antennae longer than their head, and a constricted waist that connects their thorax and abdomen. Body color may be dark, metallic gold, green, or blue, sometimes with stripes on the abdomen. Some species are very hairy, and females have long hairs on their hind legs and thorax, modified for carrying large quantities of pollen.

WHERE THEY ARE FOUND: Bees can be found on flowers, including wildflowers and blooms of flowering shrubs and trees. Ground-nesting bees construct nests in soils of their preference. Many prefer sandy or loamy soils, but some will nest in clayey soils. Some have very specific soil preferences—the alkali bee (*Nomia melanderi*), for example, nests in subirrigated alkaline soil. Different species also have preferences regarding nest depth and architecture.

WHAT THEY EAT: Ground-nesting bee larvae consume provisions of pollen and nectar within the nest. Adults drink nectar from flowers.

LIFE CYCLE: These bees lay eggs within a chamber that's filled with food supplies and located in a subterranean nest. Larvae consume their provisions quickly and enter a resting phase as a prepupae or pupae. Some species have a single generation per year, while others have several. Those species that

FIGURE 245—Green sweat bee (*Agapostemon virescens*) excavating nest.

FIGURE 246—Mining bee (*Andrena* sp.) on a blueberry flower.

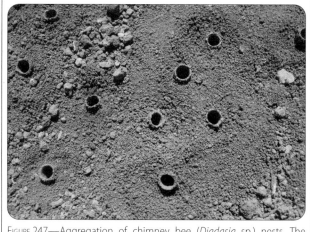

FIGURE 247—Aggregation of chimney bee (*Diadasia* sp.) nests. The center nest is dusted with sunflower pollen.

FIGURE 248—Some specialist bee species, like the squash bee (*Peponapis* sp.), nest directly under their host plants.

GROUND-NESTING BEES

have one generation are only on the wing as adults for three to six weeks, emerging during a particular season. Bees that specialize on the pollen of certain plant species will time their emergence with the flowering of the plant.

Most species are solitary, and the female constructs her nest and collects provisions for her young alone. Some species form semi-social colonies where they live cooperatively with their sisters, and others form primitively social colonies with some division of labor.

APPROX. NUMBER OF KNOWN SPECIES: 15,000 worldwide (2,900 in the United States).

RELATIVE ABUNDANCE: Some bees can nest in huge aggregations with thousands of individuals sharing a good nest site. When this happens, there may be two or three dozen nests per square foot.

NOTES OF INTEREST:

- Some species visit a wide range of flowers to collect pollen, while others only collect pollen from a small subset of flowering plants.
- Most bees are solitary and are very docile, avoiding defense of their nest. The name "tickle bee" was coined by students at a Portland, Oregon, elementary school where tens of thousands of mining bees nest in their playing field. The children would catch the bees during recess and said they tickled in their hands.
- The nests of cellophane bees (*Colletes* spp.) are lined with a distinctive cellophane-like substance to protect their growing offspring from water and mold. The cell lining, made from saliva and a secretion from a gland on the bee's abdomen, makes the cells waterproof, and these bees often nest near creeks.
- Male bees do not have a nest to return to at night and will sleep on plants, often in clusters, clamping their jaws around the stem and resting until morning.
- Sweat bees, in the family Halictidae, will lick sweat from human skin to obtain salt.

FIGURE 249—Excavated nest with close-up of bee larva in nest cell.

- Reducing tillage can support ground-nesting bees, as can on-farm flowering plant habitat. Beware that tillage that reaches a depth of 6–12" (15.2–30.5 cm) may destroy part or all of some bee nests.
- A few bees in the family Megachilidae will create shallow nests in the soil and use plant materials such as leaves or resins in their nest construction.

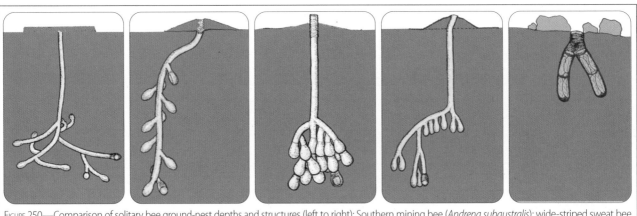

FIGURE 250—Comparison of solitary bee ground-nest depths and structures (left to right): Southern mining bee (*Andrena subaustralis*); wide-striped sweat bee (*Halictus farinosus*); sunflower chimney bee (*Diadasia enavata*); alkali bee (*Nomia melanderi*); and tooth-footed leafcutter bee (*Megachile dentitarsus*)

70. BUMBLE BEES

PHYLUM: Arthropoda » **CLASS:** Insecta » **ORDER:** Hymenoptera » **FAMILY:** Apidae » **GENUS:** *Bombus*

SIZE: 0.39–1.06" (10–27 mm).

ECOLOGICAL ROLE: Bumble bee queens move soil when they dig burrows for overwintering, as well as occasionally in the construction of their nests. Bumble bees are critically important pollinators of crops and wild trees, shrubs, and wildflowers.

DESCRIPTION: Bumble bees are robust and have extremely hairy or fuzzy black-and-yellow bodies, sometimes with additional orange, red, white, or brown. They have long antennae and membranous wings.

WHERE THEY ARE FOUND: Queens select an existing insulated cavity in or above the ground. Nest sites include old rodent burrows or cavities beneath a clump of bunch grass. In the winter, queens hibernate in shallow underground burrows, often under forest humus, at the base of shrubs, or in rock or brush piles. Adults visit the flowers of a vast range of wildflowers, shrubs, and trees.

WHAT THEY EAT: Larvae consume a mix of pollen and nectar, and adults drink nectar.

LIFE CYCLE: Bumble bees are social insects that live in colonies of 25 to 400, founded by a queen. Mated queen bumble bees hibernate through winter, initiate a nest in early spring, and then forage widely to provision that nest. Worker bees, the daughters of the queen, help in nest building, brood rearing, and defense of the nest as the colony grows in size through spring and summer. In late summer and autumn, new queens and males are reared and leave their nests to find mates. Males, workers, and old queens will die when winter arrives.

APPROX. NUMBER OF KNOWN SPECIES: 260 worldwide (46 in North America).

RELATIVE ABUNDANCE: Data unavailable.

NOTES OF INTEREST:

- Bumble bees are critically important pollinators of wild plants and many blooming crops.
- Bumble bees can generate internal body heat by shivering their flight muscles, which allows them to be active in cooler weather. As a group, they are more diverse in cooler climates or at high altitudes than in warmer climates.
- An older name for these bees is humble bees, because of the humming noise they make while flying. And, for Harry Potter fans, dumbledore is an 18th-century word for bumble bee.
- Not all bumble bees make a nest: several species are nest parasites of other *Bombus* species.
- Permanent habitat on farms can support bumble bees.

FIGURE 251—Bumble bee on gayfeather (*Liatris* sp.).

FIGURE 252—Bumble bee carrying pollen into her underground nest.

FIGURE 253—Brown-belted bumble bee (*Bombus griseocollis*) queen incubating her first generation of worker daughters.

BUMBLE BEES

GROUND-NESTING PREDATORY WASPS

71. GROUND-NESTING PREDATORY WASPS

PHYLUM: Arthropoda » **CLASS:** Insecta » **ORDER:** Hymenoptera » **FAMILIES:** Sphecidae, Vespidae
SIZE: 0.39–1.2" (10–30 mm).

ECOLOGICAL ROLE: Ground-nesting predatory wasps fit into soil food webs and aboveground food webs as predators of soil animals and as pollinators of some flowering plants. Those that build nests in the ground also move and mix soils. Predatory wasps are important in agricultural systems, as they contribute to the control of some crop pests.

DESCRIPTION: Adult wasps in the family Vespidae have a notch along the inner margin of their eyes, a thin waist, and are black or brown with white, yellow, red, or orange markings. Vespid wasps fold their wings in half when at rest (they appear to have only one thin pair of wings). Adults in the family Sphecidae have a very thin, elongated waist, and are fully black, slightly metallic, or black with red, yellow, or white markings. Sphecid wasps tend to be slenderer than vespid wasps and do not have notched eyes.

FIGURE 254—Sand wasp carrying a paralyzed stinkbug into her nest.

WHERE THEY ARE FOUND: Many ground-nesting predatory wasp species construct underground nests, in which their young develop. Some species also construct nests out of clay or inside stems or cavities above ground. All sphecid wasps and most vespid wasps are solitary, with each individual female constructing and provisioning her nest; these wasps do not defend their nests. Yellowjackets (*Vespula* spp.) are social, forming colonies with a queen and dividing labor among female workers; these wasps can be aggressive in defending their nests, which are built inside existing burrows in the ground. Adults are found on flowers or searching for prey on the soil, in leaf litter, or on vegetation.

WHAT THEY EAT: Adult females collect prey to bring back to their nests as food for their carnivorous larvae. Some species are generalists, feeding on a variety of insects, and others may hunt more selectively on particular pest groups such as grasshoppers, caterpillars, or aphids. Adult wasps feed primarily on nectar, although some species also feed on rotting fruit or the juices of prey.

LIFE CYCLE: Ground-nesting predatory wasps lay eggs in a chamber within a nest, adding prey as a food source. Some species have only one generation a year, while others have multiple.

APPROX. NUMBER OF KNOWN SPECIES: 5,000 Vespidae worldwide (320 in North America) and 800 Sphecidae worldwide (125 in North America).

RELATIVE ABUNDANCE: Data unavailable.

FIGURE 255—Sand wasp adult nectaring on mountain mint (*Pycnanthemum virginianum*).

FIGURE 256—Sphecid wasp (*Sphex* sp.) dragging a katydid into her nest.

FIGURE 257—Cicada killer wasp (*Sphecius speciosus*) adult.

NOTES OF INTEREST:

- Sphecid wasps stock the nest with whole, paralyzed prey. Vespid wasps chew their prey to a pulp before taking it to the nest.
- Sand wasps (*Bycertes* and *Bembix*) nest in sandy soils, and mothers continuously bring food to their growing larvae. One larval sand wasp can eat as many as 30 stink bugs.
- Cicada killer wasps (*Sphecius*) are large, striking wasps with black-and-yellow coloration. Female wasps paralyze cicadas, which they then carry back to their underground burrows. Sometimes you can see the wasps carry the cicada partway up a tree to gain altitude before flying back to their nest with their heavy load.
- Flowering plant habitat can support adults as well as their contributions to conservation biocontrol.

FIGURE 258—Yellowjacket exiting underground nest.

· ·

72. VELVET ANTS

PHYLUM: Arthropoda » **CLASS:** Insecta » **ORDER:** Hymenoptera » **FAMILY:** Mutillidae
SIZE: 0.23–1.2" (6 mm–3 cm).
ECOLOGICAL ROLE: Velvet ants, a group of wasps, are external parasitoids on some soil insects, feeding on and killing their hosts.
DESCRIPTION: These wasps have skinny waists and resemble ants, but they are very hairy and usually brightly colored with orange, red, yellow, or black hairs. Females are wingless and have stingers, while males have wings and are stingless.
WHERE THEY ARE FOUND: Larvae are underground with their hosts. Adult females can be seen on the soil surface, and males are sometimes found on flowers.
WHAT THEY EAT: These wasps primarily parasitize ground-nesting bees and wasps but may also attack a few other soil-dwelling insects. Adults eat nectar.
LIFE CYCLE: Female velvet ants dig through soil or break into mud nests to find their hosts. Then, velvet ants lay eggs on the surface of their host's body. Larvae hatch and consume their hosts (which are usually in the larval stage) within a few days. Larvae then spin cocoons and pupate; most species overwinter as pupa. Velvet ants have one generation a year.
APPROX. NUMBER OF KNOWN SPECIES: 8,000 worldwide (483 in North America).
RELATIVE ABUNDANCE: Data unavailable.
NOTES OF INTEREST:

- Females are sometimes called cow killers because of their powerful stings, which have been reported to be among the most painful of insect stings.
- Females also have extra hard exoskeletons to help ward off the defense attempts of hosts.
- Velvet ants squeak to deter predators.

FIGURE 259—Female red velvet ant (*Dasymutilla occidentalis*).

FIGURE 260—Male velvet ant (*Sphaeropthalma pensylvanica*).

73. PARASITOID WASPS

PHYLUM: Arthropoda » CLASS: Insecta »
  ORDER: Hymenoptera » SUPERFAMILIES:
  Chalcidoidea*, Ichneumonoidea*
  * *There are additional parasitoid wasp superfamilies, but*
    these two contain by far most of the species of internal
    parasitoids.
SIZE: 0.06–0.8" (1–20 mm).
ECOLOGICAL ROLE: These wasps are internal parasitoids
  of soil arthropods, living on and killing their hosts.
  There are also many species that live aboveground that
  are important in agricultural systems, contributing to
  the control of crop pests.
DESCRIPTION: As adult wasps, some species are extremely
  tiny while others are more sizable. Although this may
  be hard to see, these wasps all have slender bodies with
  narrow waists. Many parasitoids of soil insects have no
  wings. Females have an ovipositor, a long, stinger-like
  appendage used to deposit eggs into hosts, though it
  is less visible in some species.
WHERE THEY ARE FOUND: Larvae live within their
  hosts. Adults can be found on flowers with shallow
  nectar reserves.
WHAT THEY EAT: Many parasitoid wasps are host
  specific and are highly effective in regulating the
  populations of certain pests. Hosts include eggs,
  larvae, or adults of soil insects (and many other
  insects, including parasitoid wasps themselves). The
  life cycle of parasitoid wasps is closely synchronized
  to that of their hosts. An adult female wasp finds a
  host at the appropriate life stage and deposits one
  or several eggs on, inside, or near the host. The
  larvae develop on or inside the host, feeding on it,
  but usually not killing the host until the wasp larvae
  reach maturity and pupate. Adult wasps emerge and
  seek new hosts to repeat the cycle.

FIGURE 261—*Diapetimorpha introita* wasp parasitizing corn earworm pupa.

FIGURE 262—Wingless parasitoid wasp.

LIFE CYCLE: Parasitoid wasps lay eggs on the surface of or inserted inside a host's body.
  These wasps overwinter as an egg or larva within their host, as a pupa within their
  cocoon, or as adults.
APPROX. NUMBER OF KNOWN SPECIES: 42,000 in the superfamily Ichneumonoidea
  worldwide (5,000 in North America) and 22,000 in the superfamily Chalcidoidea
  worldwide (2,600 in North America). Estimates for both superfamilies are significantly
  higher (500,000 species worldwide), but most remain undescribed.
RELATIVE ABUNDANCE: Data unavailable.
NOTES OF INTEREST:

FIGURE 263—Tiny *Muscidifurax raptor* parasitizing house fly puparium.

- These wasps need habitat that provides nectar sources for adults, as well as habitat for their hosts.
- Species diversity of parasitoid wasps is extremely high. Parasitoid wasps probably have more species than any other
  insect group. An estimated 15% of all insects are parasitic on other arthropods. There are even parasitoid wasps that
  parasitize other parasitoid wasps; these are known as hyperparasitoids.

PARASITOID WASPS

FIGURE 264—Diverse vertebrate species—from the gopher tortoise, a keystone species in the Southeast (left), to neighborly ground squirrels and burrowing owls (right)—are important contributors to soil health in their ecosystems.

Vertebrates

In terms of biomass and species diversity, vertebrate animals are the smallest portion of soil life. Some species live entirely in the soil, while most are in the soil for a portion of their life. Across North America, a diversity of vertebrate animals are part of the underground soil world: toads, salamanders, skinks, snakes, turtles, tortoises, burrowing owls, bank swallows, armadillos, moles, shrews, kangaroo rats, deer mice, voles, pocket mice, woodchucks, rabbits, gophers,

Pests and Soil Life

A small minority of the animals that live all or part of their lives in soil are pests to agriculture. Nematodes are a diverse group: some nematode species provide beneficial functions such as pest control as predators, while others are pests themselves because they feed on plant roots. Slugs can be devastating to seedling crops, especially when the use of neonicotinoid-treated seeds kills off the natural insect predators of slugs. Many of the larvae that feed on seeds, seedlings, or developing crops are moth or butterfly caterpillars. Other soil-dwelling animal groups with species that can be agricultural pests include wireworms, aphids and mealy bugs, herbivorous scarab beetles and root weevils, thrips, and symphylans.

Soil-dwelling pests can be difficult to monitor; the best management practices for reducing soil pest pressure focus on increasing biological diversity and supporting the predatory arthropods that keep pests in check. The diversity and complexity of animal communities that develop and thrive under soil health practices are essential to balancing pest populations through natural predation and disease. More diverse plant communities aboveground support more diverse invertebrate communities belowground. Practices such as poly cropping, cover cropping, rotating crops, and creating annual and perennial habitat areas break up monocultures and make it difficult for potential pests to find host plants.

FIGURE 265—Providing diverse plant communities encourages natural pest control by attracting diverse predators.

ground squirrels, chipmunks, prairie dogs, badgers, skunks, foxes, and coyotes. Soil vertebrates burrow for cover from predators, for nests to raise young, for protection from weather, for hunting other animals as food, for eating plant parts, and for storing food caches. In these roles, they contribute to cycling organic materials and nutrients in the soil profile.

After a burrow has been abandoned by the original animal, it becomes habitat for smaller animals. For example, the deep burrows of the gopher tortoise (*Gopherus polyphemus*), native to the southeastern United States, provide habitat for more than 350 other species. Bumble bees often use and rely on abandoned cavities and burrows from larger animals as nest sites to raise a new generation of bumble bees each summer. Birds such as bank swallows and burrowing owls nest in the soil, and many birds probe shallowly in the soil with their beaks to feed on soil animals and seeds.

References

Arnett Jr., R. H., 2000. *American insects: a handbook of the insects of America north of Mexico*. Crc Press.

Barbero, E., C. Palestrini, and A. Rolando. 1999. Dung beetle conservation: effects of habitat and resource selection (Coleoptera: Scarabaeoidea). *Journal of Insect Conservation* 3(2): 75–84.

Blakemore, R. 2018. Critical Decline of Earthworms from Organic Origins under Intensive, Humic SOM-Depleting Agriculture. *Soil Systems* 2(2): 33.

Borror, D. J., C. A. Triplehorn, and N. F. Johnson. 1989. *An introduction to the study of insects (No. Ed. 6)*. Saunders College Publishing.

Chan, K. Y. 1987. An overview of some tillage impacts on earthworm population abundance and diversity—implications for functioning in soils. *Soil and Tillage Research* 57 (4): 179–191.

Chichester, L. F., and L. L. Getz. 1973. The terrestrial slugs of northeastern North America. *Sterkiana* 51(2): 11–42.

Coleman, D. C., and D. H. Wall. 2007. Fauna: The Engine for Microbial Activity and Transport. In: *Soil Microbiology, Ecology, and Biochemistry. 3rd Edition*. Edited by E. A. Paul. Elsevier Academic Press. 532 pp.

Coleman, D. C., D. A. Crossley, Jr., and P. F. Hendrix. 2004. *Fundamentals of Soil Ecology. 2nd Edition*. Elsevier Academic Press. 404 pp.

Didden, W. A. M. 1990. Involvement of Enchytraeidae (Oligochaeta) in soil structure evolution in agricultural fields. *Biology and Fertility of Soils* 9(2): 152–158.

Edwards, C. A. 2004. *Earthworm Ecology*. CRC press. 456 pages.

Eisenbeis, G., and W. Wichard. 1987. *Atlas on the Biology of Soil Arthropods*. Springer-Verlag. 448 pp.

Eisenhauer, N. 2010. The action of an animal ecosystem engineer: identification of the main mechanisms of earthworm impacts on soil microarthropods. *Pedobiologia* 53(6): 343–352.

Forbes, A. A., R. K. Bagley, M. A. Beer, A. C. Hippee, and H. A. Widmayer. 2018. Quantifying the unquantifiable: why Hymenoptera—not Coleoptera—is the most speciose animal order. *BMC Ecology* doi: 10.1186/s12898-018-0176-x.

Gagbarli, E., D. Goggioli, F. Tarchi, S. Guidi, R Nannelli, N. Vignozzi, G. Valboa, M. R. Lottero, L. Corino, and S. Simini. 2015. Case study of microarthropod communities to assess soil quality in different managed vineyards. *Soil* 1: 527–536.

Gupta, V. V. S. R., and G. W. Yeattes. 1997. Soil Microfauna as Indicators of Soil Health. pp. 201–233. In *Biological indicators of soil health*. Editors Pankhurst C.E., B. Doube, and V. V. S. R. Gupta. CAB International: Oxford, UK.

Hendrix, P. F. 1995. *Earthworm Ecology and Biogeography in North America*. CRC press. 256 pp.

Hendrix, P. F., and P. J. Bohlen. 2002. Exotic earthworm invasions in North America: ecological and policy implications. *Bioscience* 52(9): 801–811.

Hölldobler, B., and E. O. Wilson. 1990. *The Ants*. Harvard University Press. 746 pp.

Hotopp, K. P., T. Pearce, J. C. Nekola, J. Slapcinsky, D. C. Dourson, M. Winslow, G. Kimber, and B. Watson. 2013. *Land snails and slugs of the mid-Atlantic and northeastern United States*. Carnegie Museum of Natural History: Pittsburgh, PA.

House, G. J., and R. W. Parmelee. 1985. Comparison of soil arthropods and earthworms from conventional and no-tillage agroecosystems. *Soil and Tillage Research* 5(4): 351–360.

James, M. T. 1960. The Soldier Flies or Stratiomyidae of California. *Bulletin of the California Insect Survey* 6(5): 79–122.

Jass, J., and B. Klausmeier. 2000. Endemics and immigrants: North American terrestrial isopods (Isopoda, Oniscidea) north of Mexico. *Crusaceana-International Journal of Crustacean Research*. 73(7): 771–800.

Jones, M. S., Z. Fu, J. P. Reganold, D. S. Karp, T. E. Besser, J. M. Tylianakis, and W. E. Snyder. 2019. Organic farming promotes biotic resistance to foodborne human pathogens. *Journal of Applied Ecology*. 56(5): 1117–1127.

Kagoshima, H., K. Kito, T. Aizu, T. Shin-i, H. Kanda, S. Kobayashi, A. Toyoda, A. Fujiyama, Y. Kohara, P. Convey, and H. Niki. 2012. Multi-decadal survival of an Antarctic nematode, Plectus murrayi, in a-20 C stored moss sample. *CryoLetters* 33(4): 280–288.

King, J. G., and P. K. Lago. 2012. The variegated mud-loving beetles (Coleoptera: Heteroceridae) of Mississippi and Alabama, with discussion and keys to the species occurring in the southeastern United States. *Insecta Mundi* 0275: 1–53.

Lartey, R. T., E. A. Curl, and C. M. Peterson. 1994. Interactions of mycophagous Collembola and biological control fungi in the suppression of Rhizoctonia solani. *Soil Biology and Biochemistry* 26(1): 81–88.

Lavelle, P. 1988. Earthworm activities and the soil system. *Biology and Fertility of Soils* 6(3): 237–251.

Lavelle, P., T. Decaëns, M. Aubert, S. Barot, M. Blouin, F. Bureau, P. Margerie, P. Mora, and J. P. Rossi. 2006. Soil invertebrates and ecosystem services. *European Journal of Soil Biology* 42: S3–S15.

Lee-Mäder, E., J. Hopwood, L. Morandin, M. Vaughan, and S. Hoffman

Black. 2014. *Farming with Native Beneficial Insects*. Storey Publishing: North Adams, MA.

Levi, H. W., and L. R. Levi. 2001. *Spiders and Their Kin*. St. Martin's Press: New York. 160 pp.

Leistikow A., and J. W. Wägele. 1999. Checklist of the terrestrial isopods of the New World (Crustacea, Isopoda, Oniscidea). *Revista Brasileira de Zoologia* 16: 1–72.

Lomolino, M. V., J. C. Creighton, G. D. Schnell, and D. L. Certain. 1995. Ecology and conservation of the endangered American burying beetle (Nicrophorus americanus). *Conservation Biology* 9(3): 605–614.

Losey, J. E., and M. Vaughan. 2006. The economic value of ecological services provided by insects. *Bioscience* 56(4): 311–323.

Maldonado, B. M., J. N. Aranibar, A. M. Serrano, N. P. Chacoff, and D. P. Vazquez. 2019. Dung beetles and nutrient cycling in a dryland environment. *Catena* 179: 66–73.

Marshall, S. A. 2006. *Insects: their natural history and diversity: with a photographic guide to insects of eastern North America*. Firefly Books: Richmond Hill, Ont.

Nardi, J. B. 2007. *Life in the soil: a guide for naturalists and gardeners*. University of Chicago Press. 336 pp.

O'Connor, B. 2009. Mites. In: Resh, V. H., and R. T. Cardé, eds. 2009. *Encyclopedia of Insects*. Academic Press.

Orgiazzi, A., R. D. Bardgett, E. Barrios, V. Behan-Pelletier, M. J. I. Briones, J. L. Chotte, G. B. De Deyn, P. Eggleton, N. Fierer, T. Fraser, K. Hedlund, S. Jeffrey, N. C. Johnson, A. Jones, E. Kandeler, N. Kaneko, P. Lavelle, P. Lemanceau, L. Miko, L. Montanarella, F. M. de Souza Moreira, K. S. Ramirez, S. Scheu, B. K. Singh, J. Six, W. H. van der Putten, and D. H. Wall. 2016. *Global Soil Biodiversity Atlas*. European Commission, Publications Office of the European Union, Luxembourg. www.globalsoilbiodiversity.org/atlas-introduction.

Roulston, T. A. H., and K. Goodell. 2011. The role of resources and risks in regulating wild bee populations. *Annual Review of Entomology* 56: 293–312.

Sands, B., and R. Wall. 2018. Sustained parasiticide use in cattle farming affects dung beetle functional assemblages. *Agriculture, Ecosystems & Environment* 265: 226–235.

Scherney, F. 1961. Contributions to the biology and economic importance of predatory beetle species: observations and experiments on wintering, activity and diet of ground beetles (Carabidae). *Journal of Applied Entomology* 48 (1–4): 163–175.

Schlaghamerský, J. 2014. A brief history of research on potworms (Annelida: Clitellata: Enchytraeidae) of North America. *Advances in Earthworm Taxonomy VI (Annelida: Oligochaeta)*. Kasparek Verlag, Heidelberg. pp. 59–70.

Sharley, D. J., A. A. Hoffmann, and L. J. Thomson. 2008. The effects of soil tillage on beneficial invertebrates within the vineyard. *Agricultural and Forest Entomology* 10(3): 233–243.

Shatilovich, A. V., A. V. Tchesunov, T. V. Neretina, I. P. Grabarnik, S. V. Gubin, T. A. Vishnivetskaya, T. C. Onstott, and E. M. Rivkina, 2018 Viable nematodes from late Pleistocene permafrost of the Kolyma river lowland. In *Doklady Biological Sciences* Vol. 480, No. 1: 100–102. Pleiades Publishing.

Shearin, A. F., S. C. Reberg-Horton, and E. R. Gallandt. 2014. Direct effects of tillage on the activity density of ground beetle (Coleoptera: Carabidae) weed seed predators. *Environmental Entomology* 36(5): 1140–1146.

Shelley, R. 1999. Centipedes and Millipedes with Emphasis on North America Fauna. *Kansas School Naturalist* 45(3).

Skevington, J. H., M. M. Locke, A. D. Young, K. Moran, W. J. Crins, and S. A. Marshall. 2019. *Field Guide to the Flower Flies of Northeastern North America*. Princeton Field Guides. 512 pp.

Steiner, G., and F. E. Albin. 1946. Resuscitation of the nematode Tylenchus polyhypnus, n. sp., after almost 39 years' dormancy. *Journal of the Washington Academy of Sciences* 36(3): 97–99.

Stinner, B. R., and G. J. House. 1990. Arthropods and other invertebrates in conservation-tillage agriculture. *Annual Review of Entomology* 35(1): 299–318.

Taylor, C. A., G. A. Schuster, J. E. Cooper, R. J. DiStefano, A. G. Eversole, P. Hamr, H. H. Hobbs III, H.W. Robison, C. E. Skelton, and R. F. Thoma. 2007. A reassessment of the conservation status of crayfishes of the United States and Canada after 10+ years of increased awareness. *Fisheries* 32(8): 372–389.

Ubick, D., P. Paquin and P. E. Cushing. 2017. *Spiders of North America: an identification manual*. American Arachnological Society.

Van Den Hoogen, J., S. Geisen, D. Routh, H. Ferris, W. Traunspurger, D. A. Wardle, R. G. De Goede, B. J. Adams, W. Ahmad, W. S. Andriuzzi, and R. D. Bardgett. 2019. Soil nematode abundance and functional group composition at a global scale. *Nature* 572(7768): 194–198.

Wallwork, J. A. 1970. *Ecology of Soil Animals*. McGraw-Hill: London. 283 pp.

Wilson, E. O. 1971. *The Insect Societies*. Harvard University Press. 562 pp.

Yearbook of the United States Department of Agriculture 1914. 1915. United States Department of Agriculture. 769 pp. Available at: https://archive.org/details/yoa1914/page/n1/mode/2up. Accessed March 2020.

7

Final Thoughts

Soil is a living, dynamic habitat for a great diversity of animals and plants. It supports the global carbon and nitrogen cycles. Healthy soils sequester carbon, helping to mitigate climate change. Likewise, the vegetation, organic matter, and good structure associated with healthy soils is a sponge for water, absorbing, filtering, and releasing it gradually over time, mitigating the effects of extreme rainfall and drought and cleaning the groundwater that we use for drinking and irrigation. Soil is fundamental for pollinators—more than 70% of native bees nest in the soil, and the plants that are codependent with pollinators grow in soil. Soil is the habitat for beneficial insects like generalist predator beetles and multitudes of other fascinating and important animals. We continue to learn more about the complexity of interactions between the living and non-living features below the surface, from plants, animals, and fungi to soil physical and chemical properties. The more we learn, the more we understand that soil is an irreplaceable part of life.

FIGURE 266—In concept and in practice, the variety of plants and animals above ground and those that are below ground are interdependent.

NRCS Conservation Practices That Can Be Used to Support Soil Organisms

SOURCES: This table was derived directly from USDA NRCS conservation practice standards; the language used is specific to NRCS practices at the time of publication (March 2023). For more information about these and other conservation practices, visit national practice standards available through the electronic Field Office Technical Guide (FOTG) at **https://efotg.sc.egov.usda.gov**. Lists and PDFs for each practice are also available at **https://www.nrcs.usda.gov/resources/guides-and-instructions/conservation-practice-standards** or your local NRCS field office.

CONSERVATION PRACTICE	CODE	DEFINITION	PURPOSE. Each practice is used to accomplish one or more of the following purposes:
Access Control	472	The temporary or permanent exclusion of animals, people, vehicles, and equipment from an area.	• Achieve and maintain desired resource conditions by monitoring and managing the intensity of use by animals, people, vehicles, and equipment in coordination with the application schedule of practices, measures, and activities specified in the conservation plan. Note: Access Control is often applied with conservation practices like Prescribed Grazing (528) or Tree/Shrub Establishment (612).
Alley Cropping	311	Trees or shrubs are planted in sets of single or multiple rows with agronomic, horticultural crops or forages produced in the alleys between the sets of woody plants that produce additional products.	• Enhance microclimatic conditions to improve crop or forage quality and quantity • Reduce surface water runoff and erosion • Improve soil health by increasing utilization and cycling of nutrients • Alter subsurface water quantity or water table depths • Enhance wildlife and beneficial insect habitat • Increase crop diversity • Decrease offsite movement of nutrients or chemicals • Increase carbon storage in plant biomass and soils • Develop renewable energy systems • Improve air quality
Conservation Cover	327	Establishing and maintaining permanent vegetative cover.	• Reduce sheet, rill, and wind erosion and sedimentation • Reduce groundwater and surface water quality degradation by nutrients and surface water quality degradation by sediment • Reduce emissions of particulate matter (including particulate matter precursors and greenhouse gases) • Enhance wildlife and pollinator and beneficial organism habitat • Improve soil health

Table 1. NRCS Conservation Practices That Can Be Used to Support Soil Organisms *continued*

CONSERVATION PRACTICE	CODE	DEFINITION	PURPOSE. Each practice is used to accomplish one or more of the following purposes:
Conservation Crop Rotation	328	A planned sequence of crops grown on the same ground over a period of time (i.e., the rotation cycle).	• Reduce sheet, rill, and wind erosion • Maintain or increase soil health and organic matter content • Reduce water quality degradation due to excess nutrients • Improve soil moisture efficiency • Reduce the concentration of salts and other chemicals from saline seeps • Reduce plant pest pressures • Provide feed and forage for domestic livestock • Provide food and cover habitat for wildlife, including pollinator forage, and nesting
Contour Buffer Strips	332	Narrow strips of permanent, herbaceous vegetative cover established around the hill slope, and alternated down the slope with wider cropped strips that are farmed on the contour.	• Reduce sheet and rill erosion • Reduce water quality degradation from the transport of sediment and other waterborne contaminants downslope • Improve soil moisture management through increased water infiltration • Reduce water quality degradation from the transport of nutrients downslope
Cover Crop	340	Grasses, legumes, and forbs planted for seasonal vegetative cover.	• Reduce sheet, rill, and wind erosion • Maintain or increase soil organic matter quantity • Improve soil aggregate stability, soil organic matter quality, and habitat for soil organisms • Reduce water quality degradation by utilizing excess soil nutrients • Reduce weed and plant pest pressure • Improve moisture management • Reduce soil compaction • Supply nitrogen to the subsequent crop • Improve habitat for pollinators, beneficial organisms, or natural enemies of crop pests
Critical Area Planting	342	Establishing permanent vegetation on sites that have, or are expected to have, high erosion rates, and on sites that have physical, chemical, or biological conditions that prevent the establishment of vegetation with normal seeding/planting practices.	• Stabilize areas with existing or expected high rates of soil erosion by wind or water • Stabilize stream and channel banks, pond and other shorelines, and earthen features of structural conservation practices • Stabilize areas such as sand dunes and riparian areas
Deep Tillage	324	Performing tillage operations below the normal tillage depth to modify adverse physical or chemical properties of a soil.	• Bury or mix soil deposits from wind or water erosion or flood overwash • Reduce soil compaction by fracturing restrictive soil layers. Note: This practice applies to all land uses having adverse soil conditions which inhibit plant growth, such as compacted layers formed by field operations, restrictive layers such as cemented hardpans (duripan) in the root zone, or overwash or deposits from wind and water erosion or flooding. This practice does not apply to normal field operations and tillage methods.

Table 1. NRCS Conservation Practices That Can Be Used to Support Soil Organisms *continued*

CONSERVATION PRACTICE	CODE	DEFINITION	PURPOSE. Each practice is used to accomplish one or more of the following purposes:
Field Border	386	A strip of permanent vegetation established at the edge or around the perimeter of a field.	• Reduce erosion from wind and water and reduce excessive sediment to surface waters (soil erosion) • Reduce sedimentation offsite and protect water quality and nutrients in surface and ground waters (water quality degradation) • Provide food and cover for wildlife and pollinators or other beneficial organisms (inadequate habitat for fish and wildlife) • Reduce greenhouse gases and increase carbon storage (air quality impact) • Reduce emissions of particulate matter (air quality impact)
Filter Strip	393	A strip or area of herbaceous vegetation that removes contaminants from overland flow.	• Reduce suspended solids and associated contaminants in runoff and excessive sediment in surface waters • Reduce dissolved contaminant loadings in runoff • Reduce suspended solids and associated contaminants in irrigation tailwater and excessive sediment in surface waters.
Forage Harvest Management	511	The timely cutting and removal of forages as hay, green chop, or ensilage.	• Optimize quantity and quality of forage at the desired levels while promoting vigorous plant regrowth • Manage the species composition to enhance desirable species • Reduce excess soil nutrients • Reduce pest pressure (insects, disease, weeds, invasive plants or plant toxins) • Improve or protect wildlife and their habitat • Optimize soil microbial life and aggregate stability • Reduce soil compaction
Forest Stand Improvement	666	The manipulation of tree and shrub species composition, structure, or density to achieve desired forest conditions.	• Maintain or improve forest carbon stocks • Maintain or improve forest health and productivity • Maintain or improve forest structure and composition • Maintain or improve wildlife, fish, and pollinator habitat • Manage natural precipitation more efficiently • Reduce forest pest pressure • Reduce forest wildfire hazard
Grassed Waterway	412	A shaped or graded channel that is established with suitable vegetation to convey surface water at a non-erosive velocity using a broad and shallow cross-section to a stable outlet.	• Convey runoff from terraces, diversions, or other water concentrations without causing erosion or flooding • Prevent gully formation • Protect/improve water quality
Hedgerow Planting	422	Establishment of dense vegetation in a linear design to achieve a natural resource conservation purpose.	• Habitat, including food, cover, and corridors for terrestrial wildlife • To enhance pollen, nectar, and nesting habitat for pollinators • Food, cover, and shade for aquatic organisms that live in adjacent streams or watercourses • To provide substrate for predaceous and beneficial invertebrates as a component of integrated pest management • To intercept airborne particulate matter • To reduce chemical drift and odor movement • Screens and barriers to noise and dust • To increase carbon storage in biomass and soils • Living fences • Boundary delineation and contour guidelines

CONSERVATION PRACTICE	CODE	DEFINITION	PURPOSE. Each practice is used to accomplish one or more of the following purposes:
Herbaceous Weed Treatment	315	The removal or control of herbaceous weeds including invasive, noxious, prohibited, or undesirable plants.	• Enhance accessibility, quantity, and/or quality of forage and/or browse • Restore or release native or desired plant communities for wildlife habitat • Protect soils and control erosion • Reduce fine fuel loads and wildfire hazard • Control pervasive plant species to a desired level of treatment
Herbaceous Wind Barriers	603	Herbaceous vegetation established in narrow strips within the field to reduce wind speed and wind erosion.	• Reduce soil erosion (wind erosion: saltation, creep, and suspension) • Reduce soil particulate emissions to improve air quality. • Improve plant health by reducing crop damage by wind or wind-borne soil particles
Mulching	484	Applying plant residues or other suitable materials to the land surface.	• Improve the efficiency of moisture management • Reduce irrigation energy used in farming/ranching practices and field operations • Improve the efficient use of irrigation water • Prevent excessive bank erosion from water conveyance channels • Reduce concentrated flow erosion • Reduce sheet, rill, and wind erosion • Improve plant productivity and health • Maintain or increase organic matter content • Reduce emissions of particulate matter
Nutrient Management	590	Manage rate, source, placement, and timing of plant nutrients and soil amendments while reducing environmental impacts.	Improve plant health and productivity • Reduce excess nutrients in surface and ground water • Reduce emissions of objectionable odors • Reduce emissions of particulate matter (PM) and PM precursors • Reduce emissions of greenhouse gases (GHG) • Reduce emissions of ozone precursors • Reduce the risk of potential pathogens from manure, biosolids, or compost application from reaching surface and ground water • Improve or maintain soil organic matter
Pest Management Conservation System	595	A system that combines an integrated pest management (IPM) decision-making process with natural resource conservation to address pest and environmental impacts.	• Reduce plant pest pressure • Reduce injury to beneficial organisms • Reduce transport of pesticides to surface and ground water • Reduce emissions of particulate matter (PM) and PM precursors (chemical droplet drift) • Reduce emissions of ozone precursors (pesticide volatilizations)
Prescribed Burning	338	Planned fire applied to a predetermined area.	• Manage undesirable vegetation to improve plant community structure and composition • Manage pests, pathogens, and diseases to reduce plant pressure • Reduce wildfire hazards from biomass accumulation • Improve terrestrial habitat for wildlife and invertebrates • Improve plant and seed production, quantity, and/or quality • Facilitate distribution of grazing and browsing animals to improve forage-animal balance • Improve and maintain habitat for soil organisms and enhance soil health

Table 1. NRCS Conservation Practices That Can Be Used to Support Soil Organisms *continued*

CONSERVATION PRACTICE	CODE	DEFINITION	PURPOSE. Each practice is used to accomplish one or more of the following purposes:
Prescribed Grazing	528	Managing the harvest of vegetation with grazing and/or browsing animals with the intent to achieve specific ecological, economic, and management objectives.	• Improve or maintain desired species composition, structure and/or vigor of plant communities • Improve or maintain quantity and/or quality of forage for grazing and browsing animals' health and productivity • Improve or maintain surface and/or subsurface water quality and/or quantity • Improve or maintain riparian and/or watershed function • Reduce soil erosion, and maintain or improve soil health • Improve or maintain the quantity, quality, or connectivity
Range Planting	550	The seeding and establishment of herbaceous and woody species for the improvement of vegetation composition and productivity of the plant community to meet management goals.	• Restore a plant community to a state similar to the ecological site description reference state for the site or another desired plant community • Provide or improve forages for livestock • Provide or improve forage, browse, or cover for wildlife • Reduce erosion by wind and water • Improve water quality and quantity • Restore hydrologic function • Increase and/or stabilize carbon balance and sequestration
Residue and Tillage Management, No-Till/Strip Till/Direct Seed	329	Limiting soil disturbance to manage the amount, orientation and distribution of crop and plant residue on the soil surface year-round.	• Reduce sheet, rill and wind erosion and excessive sediment in surface waters • Reduce tillage-induced particulate emissions • Maintain or increase soil health and organic matter content • Increase plant-available moisture • Reduce energy use • Provide food and escape cover for wildlife.
Residue and Tillage Management, Reduced Till	345	Managing the amount, orientation, and distribution of crop and other plant residue on the soil surface year-round while limiting soil-disturbing activities used to grow and harvest crops in systems where the field surface is tilled prior to planting.	• Reduce sheet, rill, and wind erosion and excessive sediment in surface waters (soil erosion) • Reduce tillage-induced particulate emissions (air quality impact) • Improve soil health and maintain or increase organic matter content (soil quality degradation) • Reduce energy use (inefficient energy use)
Restoration of Rare and Declining Natural Communities	643	Reestablishment of abiotic (physical and chemical) and biotic (biological) conditions necessary to support rare or declining natural assemblages of native plants and animals.	• To restore the physical conditions and/or unique plant community on sites that partially support, or once supported, a rare or declining natural community. Application of this practice addresses resource concerns of a degraded plant condition and/or inadequate wildlife habitat.

Table 1. NRCS Conservation Practices That Can Be Used to Support Soil Organisms *continued*

CONSERVATION PRACTICE	CODE	DEFINITION	PURPOSE. Each practice is used to accomplish one or more of the following purposes:
Riparian Herbaceous Cover	390	Grasses, sedges, rushes, ferns, legumes, and forbs tolerant of intermittent flooding or saturated soils, established or managed as the dominant vegetation in the transitional zone between upland and aquatic habitats.	• Provide or improve food and cover for fish, wildlife and livestock • Improve and maintain water quality • Establish and maintain habitat corridors • Increase water storage on floodplains • Reduce erosion and improve stability to stream banks and shorelines • Increase net carbon storage in the biomass and soil • Enhance pollen, nectar, and nesting habitat for pollinators • Restore, improve or maintain the desired plant communities • Dissipate stream energy and trap sediment • Enhance stream bank protection as part of stream bank soil bioengineering practices
Silvopasture	381	Establishment and/or management of desired trees and forages on the same land unit.	• Provide forage, shade, and/or shelter for livestock • Improve the productivity and health of trees/shrubs and forages • Improve water quality • Reduce erosion • Enhance wildlife habitat • Improve biological diversity • Improve soil quality • Increase carbon sequestration and storage • Provide for beneficial organisms and pollinators
Stripcropping	585	Growing planned rotations of erosion-resistant and erosion-susceptible crops or fallow in a systematic arrangement of strips across a field.	• Reduce sheet and rill erosion • Reduce wind erosion • Reduce excess nutrients in surface waters • Reduce sediment transport to surface waters • Reduce pesticide transport to surface waters • Improve plant productivity and health
Tree/Shrub Establishment	612	Establishing woody plants by planting seedlings or cuttings, by direct seeding, and/or through natural regeneration.	• Maintain or improve desirable plant diversity, productivity, and health by establishing woody plants • Create or improve habitat for desired wildlife species compatible with ecological characteristics of the site • Control erosion • Improve water quality • Reduce excess nutrients and other pollutants in runoff and groundwater • Sequester and store carbon • Restore or maintain native plant communities • Develop renewable energy systems • Conserve energy • Provide for beneficial organisms and pollinators
Upland Wildlife Habitat Management	645	Provide and manage upland habitats and connectivity within the landscape for wildlife.	• Treating upland wildlife habitat concerns identified during the conservation planning process that enable movement, or provide shelter, cover, food in proper amounts, locations and times to sustain wild animals that inhabit uplands during a portion of their life cycle
Vegetative Barrier	601	Permanent strips of stiff, dense vegetation established along the general contour of slopes or across concentrated flow areas.	• Reduce sheet and rill erosion • Reduce ephemeral gully erosion • Reduce sediment transport to surface waters
Wildlife Habitat Planting	420	Establishing wildlife habitat by planting herbaceous vegetation or shrubs.	• Improve degraded wildlife habitat for the target wildlife species or guild • Establish wildlife habitat that resembles the historic, desired, and reference native plant community

Table 1. NRCS Conservation Practices That Can Be Used to Support Soil Organisms *continued*

CONSERVATION PRACTICE	CODE	DEFINITION	PURPOSE. Each practice is used to accomplish one or more of the following purposes:
Windbreak/ Shelterbelt Establishment	380	Establishing, enhancing, or renovating windbreaks, also known as shelterbelts, which are single or multiple rows of trees and/or shrubs in linear or curvilinear configurations.	• Reduce soil erosion from wind • Enhance plant health and productivity by protecting plants from wind-related damage • Manage snow distribution to improve moisture utilization by plants • Manage snow distribution to reduce obstacles, ponding, and flooding that impacts other resources, animals, structures, and humans • Improve moisture management by reducing transpiration and evaporation losses and improving irrigation efficiency • Provide shelter from wind, snow, and excessive heat, to protect animals, structures, and humans • Improve air quality by intercepting airborne particulate matter, chemicals, and odors, and/or by reducing airflow across contaminant or dust sources • Reduce energy use in heating and cooling buildings, and in relocating snow Increase carbon storage in biomass and soils
Woody Residue Treatment	384	The treatment of residual woody material that is created due to management activities or natural disturbances.	• Reduce hazardous fuels • Reduce the risk of harmful insects and disease • Protect/maintain air quality by reducing the risk of wildfire • To improve access for management purposes • Improve access to forage for livestock and wildlife • Develop renewable energy systems • Enhance aesthetics • Reduce the risk of harm to humans and livestock • Improve the soil organic matter • Improve the site for natural or artificial regeneration

Appendix B: Resources

Books & Publications

Bentrup, G. 2008. *Conservation Buffers: Design Guidelines for Buffers, Corridors, and Greenways.* Asheville, NC: United States Department of Agriculture, Forest Service Southern Research Station. Available at: www.fs.usda.gov/nac/buffers/index.html

Borror, D. J., and R. E. White. 1970. *A Field Guide to Insects: America North of Mexico.* Boston: Houghton Mifflin.

Masters, N. 2019. *For the Love of Soil: Strategies to Regenerate Our Food Production Systems.* New Zealand: Printable Reality.

Midwest Cover Crops Council. www.midwestcovercrops.org/

Moebius-Clune, B. N., D. J. Moebius-Clune, B. K. Gugino, O. J. Idowu, R. R. Schindelbeck, A. J. Ristow, H. M. van Es, et al. 2016. *Comprehensive Assessment of Soil Health: The Cornell Framework.* Geneva, NY: Cornell University.

Montgomery, D. R. 2007. *Dirt: The Erosion of Civilizations.* Berkeley: University of California Press.

Montgomery, D. R. 2017. *Growing a Revolution: Bringing Our Soil Back to Life.* New York: W. W. Norton.

Montgomery, D. R., and A. Biklé. 2015. *The Hidden Half of Nature: The Microbial Roots of Life and Health.* New York: W. W. Norton.

Nardi, J. B. 2009. *Life in the Soil: A Guide for Naturalists and Gardeners.* Chicago: University of Chicago Press.

Stika, J. 2016. *A Soil Owner's Manual: How to Restore and Maintain Soil Health.* Self-published, CreateSpace.

Online Resources

Cornell Soil Health Training Manual
http://soilhealth.cals.cornell.edu/training-manual/

Global Soil Biodiversity Initiative
www.globalsoilbiodiversity.org/

Northeast Cover Crops Council
http://northeastcovercrops.com/

Sustainable Agriculture Research and Education (SARE). "Cover crops."
www.sare.org/resources/cover-crops/

SARE. "What is Soil Health?"
www.sare.org/resources/what-is-soil-health/

Southern Cover Crops Council
https://southerncovercrops.org/

University of California IPM. "Bee precaution pesticide ratings."
www2.ipm.ucanr.edu/beeprecaution/

USDA Natural Resources Conservation Service (NRCS). "Soil health."
www.nrcs.usda.gov/wps/portal/nrcs/main/soils/health/

USDA NRCS. "Soil Health Assessment."
https://www.nrcs.usda.gov/conservation-basics/natural-resource-concerns/soils/soil-health/soil-health-assessment

USDA NRCS. "Soil Quality Test Kit."
https://www.nrcs.usda.gov/conservation-basics/natural-resource-concerns/soils/soil-health/soil-quality-test-kit

USDA NRCS. "Windows Pesticide Screening Tool (WIN-PST)."
https://www.nrcs.usda.gov/resources/tech-tools/windows-pesticide-screening-tool-win-pst

USDA NRCS. "Cropland In-Field Soil Health Assessment Worksheet."
https://directives.sc.egov.usda.gov/OpenNonWebContent.aspx?content=44419.wba

Xerces Society. 2017. "Beneficial Insects for Natural Pest Control: Soil Scouting."
https://xerces.org/publications/scouting-guides/beneficial-insects-for-natural-pest-control-soil-scouting

Additional Acknowledgments

Photographs and Diagrams

NOTE: The URLs for images found on Flickr are truncated for length. Complete URLs begin with www.flickr.com/photos... .

A. Zaitsev / Flickr [.../25258027@N02]—Fig. 228.

Alton N. Sparks Jr., University of Georgia / Bugwood.org—Fig. 206.

Álvaro Reguly / Flickr [.../alvaroreguly]—Fig. 3 (groundhog).

Andy Murray / Flickr [.../andybadger]—Fig. 70.

Andy Reago & Chrissy McClarren / Flickr [.../wildreturn]—Figs. 128, 150.

Anita Gould / Flickr [.../anitagould]—Fig. 187.

Arthur Rothstein, Library of Congress—Fig. 2.

Beverly Skinner, USFWS Mountain-Prairie Region / Flickr [.../usfwsmtnprairie]—Fig. 18.

Brenda Dobbs / Flickr [.../bugldy99]—Front cover (*web version*—oribatid mite, springtail; *press version*—springtail); Figs. 67, 75, 76, 91, 92, 107, 117, 136, 197.

Brian Gratwicke / Flickr [.../briangratwicke]—Fig. 23.

Bryan Reynolds—Figs. 9, 10, 11, 17.

Candace Fallon / The Xerces Society—Fig. 266 (ground-nesting bee).

Candy Thomas / USDA—Figs. 48, 49, 50.

Carlos Enrique Hermosilla / Flickr [.../26925527@N07]—Fig. 126.

Carmen Champagne / BugGuide [bugguide.net/user/view/15231]—Fig. 141.

Conservation Cropping Sistems Initiative [www.ccsin.org]—Fig. 41.

Ceridwen / Flickr [.../tiggywinkle]—Fig. 86.

Chih-Han Chang, Johns Hopkins University, Smithsonian Environmental Research Center / Flickr [.../serc_biodiversity]—Fig. 78.

Chris Evans, University of Illinois / Bugwood.org—Fig. 131.

Christina Butler / Flickr [.../144198875@N02]—Figs. 127, 153, 210.

Christophe Quintin / Flickr [.../34878947@N04]—Fig. 61.

Clemson University USDA Cooperative Extension Slide Series / Bugwood.org—Figs. 112, 167 (eggs/larvae/pupae).

Colette Kessler, SD NRCS / Flickr [.../nrcs_south_dakota]—Front cover; Fig. 33 (Maximize Continuous Living Roots).

Cornell University—Fig. 26.

Craig Pemberton / Flickr [.../craigpemberton]—Fig. 212.

D. Fletcher / Flickr [.../dfletcher]—Fig. 96.

D. Sikes / Flickr [.../alaskaent]—Figs. 63, 109, 183.

Dalinda Bouraoui, Collection Pénard MHNG / Wikimedia Commons—Fig. 51.

Dann Thombs / Flickr [.../goshzilla]—Fig. 193.

Darin / Flickr [.../carquestguy]—Fig. 35.

David Bosch / USDA–ARS—Figs. 27, 33 (Maximize Soil Cover).

David Cappaert / Bugwood.org—Figs. 140, 151, 156, 179, 181, 182, 257.

David R. Maddison, Tree of Life Media / Wikimedia Commons—Fig. 230.

David Stephens / Bugwood.org—Fig. 104.

Dawn Dailey O'Brien, Cornell University / Bugwood.org—Fig. 208.

Dennis Briggs—Fig. 249 (main).

Derek / Flickr [.../ezra]—Fig. 79.

Diagram adapted from International Rice Research Institute (IRRI) / Flickr [.../ricephotos]—Fig. 24.

Dialectum / Wikimedia Commons—Fig. 84.

Don Loarie / Flickr [.../loarie]—Figs. 57, 58, 59, 66.

Edward Rooks / Flickr [.../edwardrooks]—Fig. 124.

Eleanor Dietrich / Flickr [.../wildflowersflorida]—Fig. 85.

Eli Sagor / Flickr [.../esagor]—Fig. 82.

Eric Lee-Mader / The Xerces Society—Fig. 266 (tumuli).

Even Dankowicz / BugGuide [bugguide.net/user/view/83955]—Figs. 64, 221.

Eyeweed / Flickr [.../eyeweed]—Fig. 116.

Fitz Clarke / Bugwood.org—Fig. 244.

Florida Fish and Wildlife / Flickr [.../myfwcmedia]—Figs. 147, 264 (left).

Frank Peairs / Bugwood.org—Fig. 95.

G. Keith Douce, University of Georgia / Bugwood.org—Fig. 121.

Garrett Duyck, NRCS Oregon / Flickr [.../nrcs_oregon]—Fig. 32.

Gary Alpert, Harvard University / Bugwood.org—Figs. 115, 118.

Gerald J. Lenhard, Louisiana State University / Bugwood.org—Fig. 214.

Hillary Sardinas / The Xerces Society—Fig. 247.

Ian Marsman / Flickr [.../imarsman]—Fig. 98.

Insects Unlocked / Flickr [.../131104726@N02]—Figs. 97, 238, 262.

J. Maughn / Flickr [.../jmaughn]—Figs. 88, 89, 264 (right).

J. Nardi, University of Chicago Press—Figs. 5, 9, 13, 16, 43, 46, 52, 60, 203 (inside burrow).

Jason Johnson, Iowa NRCS / Flickr [.../iowanrcs]—Figs. 25, 34.

Jeff Vanuga, USDA NRCS—Fig. 7.

Jennifer Hopwood / The Xerces Society— Back cover; Figs. 99, 106, 133, 186, 189, 192, 209, 222, 241, 255.

Jessa Kay Cruz / The Xerces Society—Figs. 200, 266 (orchard).

Jesse Christopherson / Flickr [.../33338468@N00]—Fig. 105.

Jessica Louque, Smithers Viscient / Bugwood.org—Figs. 132, 142.

Jim Baker, NCSU / Bugwood.org—Figs. 177, 205.

Jim Cane / USDA-ARS—Fig. 249 (insert).

Jim Jasinski OHSU Extension / Bugwood.org—Fig. 248.

Jim Occi, BugPics / Bugwood.org—Fig. 167 (adults).

Joe Berry / Bugwood.org—Fig. 178.

John Beetham / Flickr [.../dendroica]—Fig. 148.

John C. French Sr., Retired, University of Georgia–Auburn & University of Missouri / Bugwood.org—Fig. 149.

John van der Linden / BugGuide [bugguide.net/user/view/43382]—Fig. 226.

John Williams / USDA–ARS—Fig. 33 (Minimize Disturbance).

Johnny N. Dell / Bugwood.org—Figs. 159, 194.

Jon Cox / Flickr [.../154347912@N05]—Fig. 145.

Jon Richfield / Wikimedia Commons—Figs. 134, 161.

Jon Yuschock / Bugwood.org—Fig. 185.

Jonathan Coffin / Flickr [.../stonebird]—Figs. 144, 158, 240.

Joseph Berger / Bugwood.org—Figs. 102, 122, 166 (adult).

Judy Gallagher / Flickr [.../52450054@N04]—Figs. 87, 154 (female), 180, 190, 211, 259.

Justin Meissen / Flickr [.../40855483@N00]—Fig. 251.

Kansas Dept of Agriculture / Bugwood.org—Fig. 129.

Katja Schulz / Flickr [.../treegrow]—Front cover (press version—oríbatid mite, firefly larva); Figs. 65, 68, 69, 73, 74, 77, 90, 100, 152, 157, 162, 165, 170, 173, 188, 196, 202, 223, 227, 229, 231, 234, 235, 236, 237, 260.

Kay Ledbetter, Texas A&M AgriLife Communications—Fig. 28 (top).

Keith Weston / USDA—Fig. 19.

Ken Schneider / Flickr [.../zonotrichia]—Figs. 154 (male), 171, 207.

Ken Slade / Flickr [.../texaseagle]—Fig. 175.

Ken-ichi Ueda / Flickr [.../ken-ichi]—Fig. 71.

Kent McFarland / Flickr [.../vtebird]—Fig. 253.

Kerry Wixted / Flickr [.../kwixted0]—Fig. 93.

Lance Cheung, USDA / Flickr [.../usdagov]—Figs. 15, 30.

Larah McElroy / Flickr [.../larahsphotography]—Fig. 146.

Laura Pontiggia / Flickr [.../pontla]—Fig. 81.

Lynda Richardson / Virginia NRCS—Figs. 3 (probe), 21.

m-louis / Flickr [.../m-louis]—Fig. 225.

Mace Vaughan / The Xerces Society—Fig. 266 (mason bee nest).

ManDuKinGs / Flickr [.../114196068@N06]—Fig. 113.

Marc Perkins / Flickr [.../occbio]—Fig. 44.

Mark Yokoyama / Flickr [.../theactionitems]—Figs. 163, 218, 219.

Marshal Hedin / Flickr [.../23660854@N07]—Figs. 72, 111, 123.

Matthew Shepherd / The Xerces Society—Figs. 256, 266 (sphecid wasp nest, mining bee nest).

Maurice (Epitree) / Flickr [.../63394592@N08]—Fig. 114.

Microbe World / Flickr [.../microbeworld]—Fig. 53.

Mike Quinn / BugGuide [bugguide.net/user/view/27357]—Fig. 125.

Mike Reding and Betsy Anderson, USDA-ARS / Bugwood.org— Front cover (web version—wasp larva); Fig. 243.

Mizzou CAFNR / Flickr [.../cafnr]—Fig. 3 (infiltration demonstration).

Mohammed El Damir / Bugwood.org—Fig. 166 (larva/pupa).

Nancy Lee Adamson / The Xerces Society—Figs. 246, 254, 266 (sand wasp nest).

Natalie McNear / Flickr [.../midasvanderhand]—Fig. 217.

Nick Sloff, The Pennsylvania State University (from Douglas & Tooker 2012)—Fig. 83.

NRCS Oregon / Flickr [.../nrcs_oregon]—Fig. 3 (cover crop workshop).

Patrick Coin / Flickr [.../pcoin]—Figs. 199, 224.

Pennsylvania NRCS / Flickr [.../pa-nrcs]—Fig. 42.

Pest and Diseases Image Library / Bugwood.org—Fig. 169.

Pierre Bornand / Flickr [.../kahhihou]—Fig. 233.

Rich Schilk / Flickr [.../naturalista66]—Fig. 204.

Rob Wanenchak / Flickr [.../thephillyfly]—Fig. 119.

Russ Ottens, University of Georgia / Bugwood.org—Fig. 130.

Sara Morris / The Xerces Society—Figs. 103, 132, 245, 258, 266 (jumping spider, beetle larva).

Sarah Foltz Jordan / The Xerces Society—Figs. 22, 33 (Maximize Biodiversity), 45, 101, 198, 201, 265, 266 (ground beetle, tiger beetle, yellowjacket nest).

Scot Nelson / Flickr [.../scotnelson]—Fig. 40.

Scott Bauer, USDA—Fig. 261.

Scott King / Flickr [.../minnesotameadowhawk]—Fig. 203 (outside burrow).

Sean McCann / Flickr [.../deadmike]—Fig. 108.

Soil Science / Flickr [.../soilscience]—Fig. 8.

South Dakota NRCS / Flickr [.../nrcs_south_dakota]—Fig. 14.

Specious Reasons / Flickr [.../28594931@N03]—Figs. 54, 55, 56.

Stephen Luk / BugGuide [bugguide.net/user/view/7001]—Fig. 232.

Stuart Rankin / Flickr [.../24354425@N03]—Fig. 120.

Susan Ellis / Bugwood.org—Figs. 168, 172, 213, 215, 216, 220.

Tina Reynolds / Flickr [.../ksrecomm]—Fig. 1.

Tom Koerner, USFWS / Flickr [.../usfwsmtnprairie]—Fig. 94.

Tom Murray / BugGuide [bugguide.net/user/view/1368]—Fig. 174.

Tom Murray / Flickr [.../tmurray74]—Fig. 143.

Tom Potterfield / Flickr [.../tgpotterfield]—Fig. 80.

Tracy Robillard, Oregon NRCS / Flickr [.../nrcs_oregon]—Fig. 38, 39.

U.S. Geological Survey [water.usgs.gov/nawqa/pnsp/usage/maps/compound_listing.php]—Fig. 31.

Uli Lorimer / Flickr [.../53817483@N00]—Fig. 239.

United Soybean Board / Flickr [.../unitedsoybean]—Fig. 37.

USDA / Flickr [.../usdagov]—Fig. 36.

USDA NRCS Montana / Flickr [.../160831427@N06]—Fig. 4.

USDA-ARS / Bugwood.org—Fig. 263.

USDA-ARS United States National Collection of Scale Insects Photographs / Bugwood.org—Fig. 137.

Wesley Miller / South Dakota NRCS [.../nrcs_south_dakota]—Fig. 28 (bottom).

Whitney Cranshaw, Colorado State University / Bugwood.org—Figs. 62, 110, 135, 155, 160, 164, 176, 184, 191, 195, 242.

Xerces Society / Brianna Borders—Fig. 47.

Xerces Society / Justin Wheeler—Fig. 29.

Xerces Society / Sara Morris—Figs. 6; 138 & 139 (adapted from *California Fruits: How to Grow Them*); 250 (adapted from the USDA's *Insects: The Yearbook of Agriculture*).

yaquina / Flickr [.../70097310@N00]—Figs. 3 (bumble bee colony), 252.

Zug Zwang / Flickr [.../mon_oeil]—Fig. 20.

Soil Life Profiles Index